THE

MM

FACTOR

WORKBOOK

Other books by Henry Cloud and John Townsend

Boundaries
Boundaries Workbook
Boundaries video curriculum
Changes That Heal (Cloud)
Changes That Heal Workbook (Cloud)
Hiding from Love (Townsend)
Twelve "Christian" Beliefs That Can Drive You Crazy
Twelve "Christian" Beliefs That Can Drive You Crazy Workbook
Safe People
Safe People Workbook
The Mom Factor

From the Best-Selling Authors of *Boundaries*

Dr. Henry Cloud
Dr. John Townsend

THE
M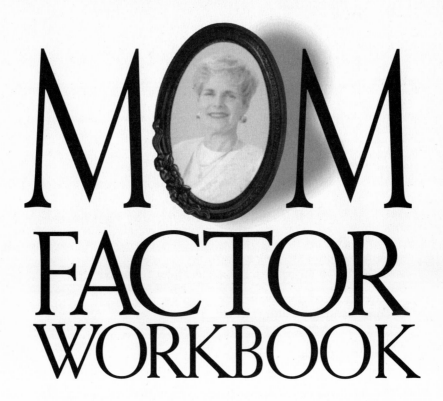M
FACTOR
WORKBOOK

Dealing with the Mother You Had,
Didn't Have, or Still Contend With

ZondervanPublishingHouse
Grand Rapids, Michigan

A Division of HarperCollinsPublishers

The Mom Factor Workbook
Copyright © 1997 by Henry Cloud and John Townsend

Requests for information should be addressed to:
📖 ZondervanPublishingHouse
Grand Rapids, Michigan 49530

ISBN: 0-310-21533-1

Published in association with Sealy M. Yates, Literary Agent, Orange, CA.

Interior design by Sherri L. Hoffman

Printed in the United States of America

97 98 99 00 01 02 03 04 /❖ DH/ 10 9 8 7 6 5 4 3 2

Contents ∾

Introduction ∾

Just as we did in the text, we want to let you know right up front what you can expect from this workbook. Simply put, the questions you find here will give you the opportunity to be honest, tell the truth, take responsibility, heal, enter into forgiveness, and grieve as you look at the mom factor in your life.

Through the years and in several different counseling situations, we have seen many people struggle because they didn't understand what to do about how they were mothered. But we have also seen miracles happen: we've seen people learn much, heal much, love much, and develop a more fruitful, more meaningful relationship with mom. We've seen reconciliation happen and people begin to enjoy better lives and better connections with their mother.

So, as we look closely at the Phantom Mom, the China Doll Mom, the Controlling Mom, the Trophy Mom, the Still-the-Boss Mom, and the American Express Mom, we hope that you will come to understand some things about yourself, your mom, and God and, as a result, find yourself stronger and your relationship with your mom healthier.

Henry Cloud, Ph.D.
John Townsend, Ph.D.

Before We Start . . . ∼

➤ ➤ ➤ Mom—or someone who played that role in your life—was right there in the middle of your becoming you. Identify the person you'll be thinking about as you work through this book.

_____

➤ ➤ ➤ What do you hope to gain from reading the text and using this workbook? Or, put differently, which of the following questions are issues for you?

___ How can I have a better present-day relationship with my own (or someone else's) mother?

___ Which of my current relationships or work problems might have been influenced by the mothering I received?

___ What went right and wrong in how I was mothered—and how did that affect the connection between my childhood and my life today?

___ How can I get beyond my past mothering problems so that I can get on with my life?

___ What's the best way for me to parent my own children?

___ Do you have other questions or issues? What are they?

_____

_____

_____

_____

_____

ONE ～

What About Mom, Anyhow?

B eth loved her mother deeply and desired more than anything to have a close, respectful relationship with her. But she felt caught: *If I honor her, I dishonor my family, and if I honor my family, I dishonor her.* You may know that dilemma all too well.

WHAT'S WRONG?*

Page 12

Most people want a comfortable, mutually satisfying friendship with their mother, but the reality falls short of the ideal.

➤ ➤ ➤ Which area(s) of "mother trouble" have you encountered?

___ Inability to communicate with her

___ Her lack of respect for your choices and values

___ Her refusal to accept your own family and friends

___ A lack of freedom to have a separate life without losing her love

___ Feeling disconnected from and misunderstood by her

___ Difficulty in saying no and confronting her

___ A need to hide your real self and be perfect

___ Perceived responsibility to make her think that she is perfect

___ Guilt when you don't take care of her as she wants you to

___ Disillusionment and conflict over her interactions with your spouse

---

*The subtitles and page numbers refer to corresponding sections and pages in the book, *The Mom Factor*.

___ Guilt over not living up to her expectations and wishes

___ Sorrow that she can't seem to comprehend your pain

___ Childlike in her presence

___ Frustration over her seeming self-absorption

___ Cringing when she treats your children in familiar hurtful ways

___ Discouraged that this list is so long

We learn our patterns of intimacy, relating, and separateness from mother, but we also learn such things as how to handle failure, troublesome emotions, expectations and ideals, and grief and loss. Dave, for instance, learned from his relationship with his mother that closeness can be dangerous. He learned to fear intimacy, and this fear greatly impacted his marriage.

➤ ➤ ➤ At this stage of *The Mom Factor*, what lessons learned from your relationship with your mother can you identify? For example, What did she teach you about patterns of intimacy, relating, and separateness? About handling failure, coping with emotions, having expectations and ideals, and dealing with grief and loss? Don't worry if the list is short or vague or even nonexistent. You're reading this book to learn about the complex and critical mother-child relationship.

_____

_____

_____

_____

DOES IT HAVE TO BE THIS WAY?

Page 14   God plans for us to learn patterns of relating from our mothers, but moms who fail to follow the plan can wreak destruction in our adult lives. God's plan of repair, however, can work change, growth, redemption, and healing.

➤ ➤ ➤ As Mark's experience illustrates, when we aren't mothered perfectly (and none of us is!), God provides others to fill in the gaps. He redeems our early experience by building on the good our mother did and by supplying basic essentials our mother may have missed.

❖ What mothering do you think you missed out on? (Again, you may not be able to answer that question at this point, and that's okay. Just keep reading.)

_____

_____

_____

❖ What, if anything, might keep you from allowing people to provide the mothering you need and teach you the patterns of relating you missed the first time around? What do you think you can do to overcome those barriers? (Again, keep reading. We'll give you some specifics.)

_____

_____

_____

_____

TWO CONSIDERATIONS

Page 15 Honesty about ourselves is key to moving toward a healthier relationship with mom. Keep that in mind as you begin looking at your relationship with your mother and the process of mothering itself.

➤ ➤ ➤ First, acknowledge that many modern pop-psychology approaches suggest that mother is the real problem. Which of the following approaches have influenced you? Be specific about the source and impact of those approaches. What has your experience shown you about the shortcomings of those approaches?

❖ Blaming parents for all of your problems

_____

_____

_____

❖ Focusing only on dredging up "pain from the past" and "getting the pain out," thinking that catharsis cures

_____

_____

_____

❖ Identifying you as a victim and commiserating with how bad mom or someone else was

_____

_____

_____

❖ Excusing behavior, lack of performance, and failure in love or work because
   of what mother failed to provide

_____

_____

_____

❖ Encouraging you to live more in the past than in the present

_____

_____

_____

❖ Arranging sessions with mom, thinking that reconciling with mom or having
   mom "own" how bad she was will finally fix the hole in your heart

_____

_____

_____

➤ ➤ ➤ Thinking that resolution will come from blaming parents, trying to get them to
change, or continuing to process the events of the past, people miss out on the
necessary character change in themselves that leads to real healing.

❖ Why is it easier to blame parents, to try to get them to change, or to continue
   processing events of the past?

_____

_____

_____

❖   Why do we often avoid making necessary changes in our own character?

_____

_____

_____

❖   Why might you be avoiding making some necessary changes in yourself?

_____

_____

_____

❖   What would it take to remove those barriers, whether internal or external?

_____

_____

_____

Working out one's relationship with one's mother is very important in the growth process, but it is not the whole picture. We must also look at the process of mothering in the present.

YOUR MOM

Page 15

Two very important issues resulting from unresolved aspects of our relationship with mother are at work every day. The first has to do with the feelings we have for our mother, the injuries we felt from her, and the needs that she didn't meet. The second issue is the dynamics and patterns of relating that we learned in our relationship with mom. The first deals with how we feel today about the past; the second deals with how we repeat patterns from the past. First, let's look at the feelings that we have toward our mother.

➤ ➤ ➤   *Leftover Feelings.* As Jim's attachment to his wife increased, his unresolved feelings about his mother began to emerge and interfere. His anger toward his mother and his feelings of being controlled, mistrusted, and dominated by his mother got displaced onto Debbie. This displacement is called transference.

❖ Is transference an issue in your life? In other words, are you directing feelings toward people in the present that are really about your mother and your relationship with her in the past? Can you identify specific situations where this is occurring?

_____

_____

_____

❖ Dealing with unresolved feelings toward our mother involves forgiveness—looking honestly at problems in a relationship, naming what went wrong, feeling the feelings, letting them go, and grieving our losses. How might you benefit from forgiving your mom? Are you ready to begin the process of forgiveness? Why or why not?

_____

_____

_____

_____

➤ ➤ ➤ *Patterns of Relating.* The second mom issue has to do with understanding the dynamics and patterns of relating that we learned in our relationship with her.

❖ When have you related to someone as Jim related to Debbie due to patterns learned from your mother?

_____

_____

_____

❖ What, if any, patterns of relating (avoidance, control, compliance, dominance, passivity, aggressiveness and overcontrol, mistrust, and so forth) that you learned from your mother are you able to identify at this point?

_____

_____

_____

Our relationship with mom needs more than forgiveness: We need to become aware of dynamics and patterns and then take steps to change them.

THE MOTHERING PROCESS

Page 18

➤ ➤ ➤ For us to become comfortable with ourselves, we need someone with whom we can be ourselves. We need acceptance and understanding, and a good mother offers that. She listens to and accepts the negative, contains it, and helps her child not feel overwhelmed. She is comfortable with her child's imperfections. The child takes her comfort into his personality, and he becomes comfortable with imperfections as well. This mothering process of acceptance integrates the child.

❖ How comfortable are you with your imperfections? List, for instance, three of your imperfections.

_____

_____

_____

❖ What does the ease or struggle with which you identified some imperfections remind you about your mother's comfort with and acceptance of your imperfections?

_____

_____

_____

❖ Susan provided Jordan with empathy and containment, a basic aspect of mothering that Jordan had not received from her own mother. Who in your life offers you mothering you did not receive from your own mother?

_____

_____

_____

Friends give to one another what mother failed to give. This is what it means to be restored to the mothering process. This book will help you find out what you have missed and encourage you to receive it from others.

RESPONDING TO MOTHERING

Page 20   Negative mothering can lead to a lifelong pattern of mistrusting people, and this mistrust affects our response to the good mothering that becomes available to us.

➤ ➤ ➤   How have you responded to the good mothering that has been around you?

❖   Have you hidden your needs and vulnerability? Become combative and aggressive? Tried to control others to show that you won't let yourself be controlled? Give a specific example.

_____

_____

_____

❖   Like Jim, have you tended to be defensive and reactive, keeping yourself from getting what you need? What encounter comes to mind?

_____

_____

_____

❖   Like Jordan, have you avoided the acceptance that has become available to you later in life? Were you so caught up in your efforts to be perfect that you didn't respond to that good mothering? Explain.

_____

_____

_____

❖   Or have you been able to respond to the light—to things like honesty, vulnerability, trust, responsibility, acceptance, forgiveness—and receive it? How have you benefited from doing so?

_____

_____

_____

➤ ➤ ➤ How would you like to respond to the mothering available to you?

_____

_____

_____

_____

➤ ➤ ➤ In what relationships do you find good mothering? If your list is short or nonexistent, recognize that you would do well to enter into a community of people who
will give what mother failed to give. (For more guidance, see *Safe People* by Dr.
Henry Cloud and Dr. John Townsend, Zondervan, 1995.)

_____

_____

_____

_____

OUR ASSUMPTIONS

Page 21

➤ ➤ ➤ Review the discussion of our three assumptions before being introduced to the
Phantom Mom in the next chapter.

❖ *Assumption #1: There is no such thing as the "good child" and the "bad
mom."* Why does it make sense that forgiveness and responsibility are key to
growth? Are you willing to forgive your mother? Why or why not? Are you
willing to take responsibility for your inappropriate responses and patterns?
Why or why not?

_____

_____

_____

_____

❖ *Assumption #2: There are preordained tasks of mothering and responses to
mothering.* What do you think the tasks of mothering are?

_____

_____

_____

_____

❖ *Assumption #3: A child needs love and limits along each step.* How did your
   mother do in the love and limits department? Did you get one without the
   other? Both? Neither? Explain.

_____

_____

_____

Now the wonderful, difficult, and challenging process of dealing with mom and
mothering can begin in earnest. Let's start with a prayer.

*God, you call me to honor my mother—but sometimes that doesn't come easily.
Use this book to bring about change, growth, and healing in me and, as a result,
in my relationship with my mother. Give me the courage to look honestly at the
problems in the relationship, to name what went wrong, to feel the feelings, to let
them go, and to grieve what I've missed. Enable me to take responsibility for myself—for my past mistakes and my present situation. And help me to receive the
good mothering that is or that becomes available to me. Amen.*

TWO ❧

The Phantom Mom

For as long as humankind has been on the earth, we have associated mothering with trust and nurture. Yet many have not received nurture and trust from their mothers. Instead of connecting safely to their mothers, they have found an emptiness and a void. As Keith put it, "It's funny, when I think of being in my house, I don't even see anyone else there. It's empty. I know that my mom was there a lot, though."

➤ ➤ ➤ What scenes (if any) from your own childhood did Keith's experience call to mind? What events and feelings did you remember as you read his story?

_____

_____

_____

_____

_____

KEITH'S LIFE SINCE THEN

Page 24

➤ ➤ ➤ Keith described his home as "emotionally empty." What would such a setting teach a child about relationships? What kinds of struggles in relationships might a child with that background face as an adult?

_____

_____

_____

_____

_____

➤ ➤ ➤ Keith's mother had not been emotionally available. Consequently, he had never learned to connect and be intimate with others. Which, if any, of the following variations on the Phantom Mom theme have you experienced?

____ Overt abuse that makes connection impossible

____ Control issues that block true connection

____ Perfectionistic demands that leave the real self alone

____ Abandonment that makes trust too dangerous

____ Difficulties in the mother's life that take her away from the child

____ Reactive mothers with whom the child cannot freely share for fear of upsetting her

When a child is raised by a Phantom Mom, he cannot develop an attachment to his mother that fosters his emotional ability to develop relationships with people.

THE NEED THAT WON'T GO AWAY

Page 25   An absent and detached mother does not meet her child's five basic needs: safety, nurture, basic trust, belonging and invitation, and someone to love.

➤ ➤ ➤ Review the discussion of a child's five basic needs (pp. 25–27). What insights did you gain into yourself and perhaps your own struggles in relationships by reading about what having these needs met means to a child? Record them below.

❖ Safety (the mother's consistent, caring, and soft and understanding attention gives the child a safe place to turn; she transforms the dangerous world into a place of safety)

_____

_____

_____

❖ Nurture (a mother's nurture is nourishment and fuel for the soul)

_____

_____

_____

❖ Basic trust (trust enables us to reach out, to depend, to need, and to see others as the source of good things)

_____

_____

_____

❖ Belonging and invitation (mothers make us feel wanted, which transfers into later feelings of worth and confidence in relationships)

_____

_____

_____

❖ Someone to love (we have a basic need to love people; if mother is not safe, we either are overwhelmed by isolation or filled with hatred)

_____

_____

_____

➤ ➤ ➤ Which of these five basic needs did your mother provide well? Which ones, if any, did you fail to receive when you were growing up?

_____

_____

_____

_____

RESULTS OF THE PHANTOM MOM

Page 28

Detachment is only one sign of Phantom mothering. Other signs show up in adult life.

➤ ➤ ➤ *Relational Problems.* Of which of the following behaviors do you see evidence in your life? Give specific examples and tell what each suggests about whether or not all the parts of your relational equipment were installed when you were growing up.

___ Shallowness in relationships
___ Aloofness
___ Withdrawal
___ Mistrust, hostility, and aggression
___ Overvaluation of relationship
___ Negative relationships
___ Choosing to be in an abusive relationship rather than in no relationship at all

_____
_____
_____
_____

➤ ➤ ➤ *Functional Problems.* Which of the following do you see evidence of in your life? Give specific examples and tell what each suggests about the mothering you received.

___ Avoiding risk
___ Being devastated by failure
___ Unable to take criticism and solve problems
___ Suffering from devastating guilt
___ Feeling estranged from your talents
___ Insecure
___ Turning normal conflicts into win-lose confrontations

_____
_____
_____
_____

➤ ➤ ➤ *Spiritual Problems.* Sometimes the ability to trust God is connected with learning trust in our earliest relationships.

❖ How similar to Marty's is your experience of establishing a relationship with God?

_____

_____

_____

_____

❖ What does your struggle—or lack of struggle—to believe that God loves you and to integrate your spiritual development into the whole of life suggest about how you were mothered?

_____

_____

_____

_____

➤ ➤ ➤ *Emotional Problems.* Which of the following do you see evidence of in your life? Give specific examples and tell what each suggests about the mothering you received.

___ Depression
___ Feelings of emptiness
___ Addictions
___ Thinking problems
___ Hopelessness and meaninglessness

_____

_____

_____

_____

If we experienced good mothering, we have a head start in relating well to others; we have resolved that the world is a safe place, and we are able to function well in it; we are able to trust God and receive his love; and we have a bedrock of emotional security. But many of us don't have these things to the degree we need them to lead healthy adult lives.

WHY ME?

Page 34 People often wonder why their mothers did not or could not love them in a way that helped them. If your mother found it difficult to feel or express love, it could be for any number of reasons, few, if any, having to do with you.

➤ ➤ ➤ Review the following list of possible reasons for your mother's limitations. Which of these do you know or suspect could have been a factor in your mother's mothering of you?

____ She lacked the connection and nurture she needed as a child.

____ She was abandoned or hurt in the past and was unable to allow herself to attach deeply to anyone, even her own child.

____ She was emotionally empty.

____ She feared intimacy—knowing and being known.

____ She was depressed and did not have the emotional energy to give.

____ She had marital pain and was being torn apart.

____ She was ill or had various other difficulties.

➤ ➤ ➤ Another possible reason why your mother couldn't be all that you needed her to be is that she chose the selfish path (as all of us do from time to time and to one degree or another). What evidence do you see of your mother's choosing not to treat others (namely, her child) as she would want to be treated?

_____

_____

_____

_____

_____

Understanding the reasons for your mother's limitations can help you have more compassion for her and help you forgive her for making selfish decisions that hurt you. The reason your mother failed to love you the way you needed to be loved had much more to do with *her* than it did with *you*.

WHAT IT LOOKS LIKE NOW

Page 35 We've looked at some of the results of the Phantom Mom in a child's life. Now consider some common scenarios of what goes on between an adult child and a detached mother.

➤ ➤ ➤ If you had or suspect you had a Phantom Mom while you were growing up, which of the following scenes—if any—comes close to what you experience now that you are an adult? How is this scene similar to and different from your present-day relationship with your mother?

____ Please Love Me. (You want to share what is going on in your life, your plans and dreams, your pain, and all the things you treasure in your heart, but mom can't connect with your feelings.)

____ Where Did the Family Go? (The parties have less and less contact, and the relationship just seems to go away.)

____ I Hate You, Don't Leave Me. (The adult child covers up his longings and feelings of disconnectedness with anger; picking a fight is generally a sign that we want something from someone.)

_____

_____

_____

_____

_____

THE SAD REALITY

Page 37 Scenarios of adult children with Phantom Moms come in many different versions, sizes, and shapes.

➤ ➤ ➤ How are you dealing with a Phantom Mom? Are you trying to make her connect with you? Are you avoiding the relationship? Is your anger covering up your longing for connection?

_____

_____

_____

_____

_____

_____

➤ ➤ ➤ What have you learned about yourself from this chapter? What have you learned about how you were mothered?

_____

_____

_____

_____

_____

_____

We have seen what detached and absent mothering looks like, what it causes, what the need is, and how it can set up a painful pattern of relating even in adulthood. The need for good mothering that God programmed into us just does not go away until it is met—the next chapter focuses on this healing.

God, I'm understanding myself more now. I'm seeing more clearly the relational, functional, spiritual, and/or emotional problems that have resulted from having a Phantom Mom. Help me have more compassion for her and help me forgive her. And I ask you to put people in my life who will meet my needs for safety, nurture, trust, belonging, and someone to love—and then help me take the risks involved in receiving from them the mothering I haven't yet received. Amen.

THREE ∼

Rebuilding Your Connection

Having identified some of the needs that may not have been met by a Phantom Mom, let's now look at steps to getting those needs met and repairing what was broken in your own mothering process.

FRUIT PROBLEMS VS. ROOT PROBLEMS

Page 40

The first step in the process of getting well from mothering problems is to recognize that the symptoms—the relational, functional, spiritual, and emotional problems we looked at in the preceding chapter—aren't the problem.

➤ ➤ ➤ What did you think and/or feel when you first read the statements, "The problem isn't that we don't feel right. It's that we truly aren't right. Something is broken or undeveloped inside our heart and soul"?

_____

_____

_____

_____

➤ ➤ ➤ Are you stuck in "symptom solving"? Where are you dealing with the "fruit" problems rather than the "root" problems? Also, is the fear of confronting the emptiness inside you keeping you from dealing with character solutions?

Identifying this truth about your actions and your fears puts you on the road to healing.

_____

_____

_____

_____

"RELATIONSHIP, RELATIONSHIP, RELATIONSHIP"

Page 41   After you've determined that the problem goes beyond the immediate pain, you'll need to seek a safe context in which to work on it. After all, it is in relationships that you can get your attachment needs met.

➤ ➤ ➤ What are some possible safe contexts in which you can work on developing such relationships?

_____

_____

_____

_____

➤ ➤ ➤ Are you hesitant about developing such relationships? If you are, why? What familiar but unhealthy patterns will you have to let go of? What losses (such as safety, autonomy, and pride) will you have to experience?

_____

_____

_____

_____

➤ ➤ ➤ Remind yourself of the possible benefits that lie on the other side of taking the risk and entering relationships.

_____

_____

_____

_____

WELCOME TO YOUR NEW HOME

Page 41   In a very real sense, this chapter is about finding a new home for the lost part of your soul. That part of you that never learned to attach, connect, and trust is still alive and waiting to be developed and nurtured.

➤ ➤ ➤   When Jesus was told that his mother and brothers were waiting to talk to him, he seized the opportunity to define *true family*. When he said, "Who is my mother and who are my brothers?" Jesus wasn't saying that Mary was a bad mom—he was redefining family as having more to do with spiritual and relational ties than blood ties. What hope do you find in this new definition of *family*?

_____

_____

_____

_____

➤ ➤ ➤   At this point, who has become family in terms of the spiritual and relational ties you share? (If no one comes to mind, where do you think you might meet such people?)

_____

_____

_____

_____

WHO IS MY FAMILY?

Page 42

➤ ➤ ➤   It's common for individuals with absent/detached mother problems to confuse proximity with intimacy. That was the case for Pam, and perhaps it is for you as well. Who among your friends meets your needs for intimate connecting?

_____

_____

_____

_____

➤ ➤ ➤ Have you learned to regard intimacy as a means to an end rather than an end in itself? Explain your attitude toward intimacy and its role in your life.

_____

_____

_____

_____

➤ ➤ ➤ In what current relationships are attachment and healthy dependency goals for you? With whom in your life have you connected for the specific purpose of connection itself? What do your answers to these two questions tell you about yourself?

_____

_____

_____

_____

➤ ➤ ➤ Jesus taught "functional" Martha that her "relational" sister, Mary, was doing the right thing by sitting at his feet. Are you more like Martha or Mary in relationships? Are you a doer or a relater? If you're a doer who wants to become a relater, where are you looking for safe people and healthy relationships? (Healthy churches, support groups, recovery-friendly relationships, and therapists who deal with attachment issues are good sources for such relationships.)

_____

_____

_____

_____

People will help you learn how to connect, thereby meeting a need that your Phantom Mom didn't meet. People will help you become relational.

WHAT DO I LOOK FOR?

Page 43   What do healthy mother types look like? Supportive people have several characteristics—some of which are universal to all six "mother styles" and some of which are unique to the absent/detached style.

➤ ➤ ➤ Review the discussion of the following traits of healthy mother types (pp. 44–47). Which of these traits were especially appealing as you read about them? Which traits do you find in a current relationship? What healing will each trait bring to your life?

❖ Warmth and empathy (No matter what you say or reveal about yourself, an empathic person is on your side and wants to help, even if she disagrees with or disapproves of what she hears.)

_____

_____

_____

❖ Nonintrusiveness (A nonintrusive helper invites the hurt parts out but doesn't chase them down.)

_____

_____

_____

❖ Drawn toward dependency (New mothering relationships need to be mutually dependent ones; they understand that comfort and grace are the fuel of life.)

_____

_____

_____

❖ Honesty (Your mothering people must be able to tell the truth about themselves and about you.)

_____

_____

_____

➤ ➤ ➤ In your own words, explain what it means that "your injured parts need the mothering relationship but not the mothering responsibility" (p. 47). Who is responsible for the remothering you need?

_____

_____

_____

_____

_____

YOUR CONNECTION TASKS

Page 47
Having the right kind of mothering people around you is only part of the healing process. Your part is to respond to these people's love, truth, and support.

➤ ➤ ➤ Review the discussion of each of the following tasks (pp. 47–51). Briefly state why each is important to your remothering process.

❖ Make four important commitments.

—Commit yourself and this entire remothering endeavor to God.
—Commit yourself to a serious attempt at the growth process.
—Commit yourself verbally to the people involved in the process.
—Commit yourself to absolute truthfulness in these relationships.

_____

_____

❖ Be vulnerable.

_____

_____

❖ Take the initiative.

_____

_____

❖ Give the process time.

_____

_____

❖ Allow dependent feelings.

_____

_____

❖   Pray and seek God.

_____

_____

❖   Be aware of your defenses (devaluation, omnipotence, avoidance).

_____

_____

➤ ➤ ➤   Which of the connection tasks you've just looked at will be particularly difficult for you?

_____

_____

_____

_____

➤ ➤ ➤   Why—and what kind of support can you find for yourself as you tackle these tasks?

_____

_____

_____

_____

"MOMWORK"

Page 51   While we are interacting with our remothering friends, we can also do some repair work with our biological mothers. If mom is alive and available, we want as much healing for that relationship as she will allow.

➤ ➤ ➤   Review the descriptions of the specific tasks of momwork (pp. 51–53). What key phrase in each description helps you understand either what is involved in each step or why each step is an important part of momwork? What truth in each description especially motivates you to do the work?

❖   Forgiveness

_____

_____

❖ Invitation

_____

_____

❖ Setting limits

_____

_____

❖ Reconciliation

_____

_____

❖ Acceptance of reality

_____

_____

➤ ➤ ➤ If mom is alive and available, which task will you choose to work on first? What will be your first step? Baby steps do count—and be sure to have your safe people supporting you.

_____

_____

_____

_____

Mom won't always respond to our momwork the way we might wish. When that's the case, we must grieve our ideal of the mom who never was and probably never will be. However, you can only let go of that wish when you are filled and connected in your remothering relationships. We are only strong enough to grieve what we've lost when we've already replaced it at some level.

THE NEW ME AND THE OLD MOM

Page 53   If you work at all of the above tasks, your present relationship with mom can go two directions, depending on your mother's response.

➤ ➤ ➤ Mom may have grown over the years and want to make a real and genuine emotional attachment with you. What encouragement and what important advice
does this possibility (described on pp. 53–54) offer you?

_____

_____

_____

_____

➤ ➤ ➤ The process of growth and reconciliation may not be mom's priority right now.
This may mean more work for you.

❖ What did you learn from Patricia's experience?

_____

_____

_____

_____

❖ Why was Patricia able to cope with her mother's wishes and follow her ther-
apist's guidance?

_____

_____

_____

_____

So how will you respond to your detached Phantom Mom? It's up to you—and
then her response is up to her.

*God, I'm learning a lot about why I'm empty inside. Now I need the courage to
confront that emptiness . . . to begin to develop safe relationships . . . and to be
vulnerable so that I can find a true family, whose spiritual and relational ties will
be stronger than blood ties. Help me be more of a relational person and less of a
functional person. Help me receive the warmth and empathy, nonintrusiveness,
dependency, and honesty that healthy mother types can offer me, so that I can
better tackle the connection tasks and momwork I need to do. Amen.*

FOUR ⁓

The China Doll Mom

Stephanie couldn't handle her daughter Vicki's infant emotions—or her toddler emotions, her little-girl emotions, or her preadolescent emotions. When, in normal kid fashion, Vicki blew up after being told she couldn't go to the movies, Stephanie collapsed into a kitchen chair. "After all the love I've given you. You'll never know how deeply you've hurt your mother," she said between gasps. Vicki was certain she'd destroyed the person who had sacrificed her very life for her daughter.

➤ ➤ ➤ What scenes (if any) from your own childhood does this story call to mind? Be specific about the emotions you felt, what they triggered in your mother, and your response to your mother's reaction.

_____

_____

_____

_____

_____

_____

_____

_____

VICKI NOWADAYS

Page 56 | Like her mother, Vicki was a caring and compassionate person. She had good friends and a job she liked. Yet, also like her mother, she avoided strong or negative emotions. Whenever she felt lonely or sad, she would withdraw from others until the feelings went away. When she was hurt or angry, she worked harder in her job. This helped her tolerate her fears of getting "out of control."

➤ ➤ ➤ Do you avoid strong or negative emotions? Do you withdraw from others when you feel lonely or sad? Do you work harder or rely on some other coping behavior when you are hurt or angry? If you answered yes to any of these questions, consider the significance of your answer(s). What did you learn about feelings—or certain feelings—when you were growing up?

_____

_____

_____

_____

Vicki was also a "problem-person magnet." She found it easy to listen to others' pain, soothe it, and bandage their wounds. In fact, that became a problem in itself as time and time again she'd drain herself helping others. Then she would assume that no one was interested in her feelings and would choose not to burden others with her feelings. She was afraid of both overwhelming them and being overwhelmed herself.

➤ ➤ ➤ Think about your life. Are you—or have you been—a magnet for problem people? Cite a specific example or two.

_____

_____

_____

_____

➤ ➤ ➤ Do you go to other people with your feelings the way others come to you? Why or why not? If not, what keeps you from sharing your feelings?

_____

_____

_____

_____

Like Vicki, you may believe that strong feelings are "bad" and destructive. And like Vicki, you may not let yourself feel them too often, much less share them with others. These beliefs may be the result of having a China Doll Mom.

WHAT'S THE PROBLEM?

Page 57

Vicki's mother was fragile. A China Doll Mom, she was unable to deal with unpleasant or stressful situations in life. This kind of mother has difficulty setting limits and controlling herself and her environment. Unprepared to handle the adult world (especially the mothering part of her life), she is as overwhelmed by her child's problems as she is with her own.

➤ ➤ ➤ The China Doll Mom quickly becomes overwhelmed when a child expresses intense emotions such as panic, rage, sadness, and fear. The strength of these feelings frightens her, and she feels at a loss to deal with both the child and the feelings. Review the different ways a China Doll Mom handles intense emotions (pp. 57–58). How did your mother handle your intense emotions? Give a specific example for each style you remember.

___ Catastrophizing
___ Withdrawing
___ Overidentifying
___ Regressing
___ Smothering and hovering
___ Shaming
___ Reacting in anger

_____

_____

_____

_____

_____

_____

OUR NEED FOR CONTAINMENT

Page 58   Our first basic human need is to make an emotional attachment to mother; the second is containment. Containment is the mothering function in which the mom literally keeps the child's feelings until he can handle them for himself.

➤ ➤ ➤ Review the discussion of emotions (pp. 58–61).

❖ "God has built emotions into our personalities for a reason: *They are a signal*" (p. 59). Why is it important for children to realize this truth?

_____

_____

_____

❖ In light of the fact that "the child doesn't just have feelings; to a large extent, he is feelings" (p. 60), why is containment necessary?

_____

_____

_____

❖ What did you learn about emotions that gives you insight about yourself as a child growing up or even as a parent or significant person in the life of a child?

_____

_____

_____

➤ ➤ ➤ Growing up calls for us to integrate our needy parts, our weak parts, and our autonomous parts (pp. 60–61). Again, what did you learn about integration that gives you insight about yourself as a child growing up or even as a parent or significant person in the life of a child?

_____

_____

_____

THE SPECIFICS OF CONTAINING

Page 61 Whether we're talking about emotions or parts of oneself, containing is a mother's task to help her child mature.

➤ ➤ ➤ Review the discussion of ways mothers contain their children (pp. 61–65). Which of the following methods did your mother use well? Give a specific example.

❖ Soothing (mom exchanges a child's scary feelings for calmness, repose, and love)

_____

_____

❖ Validating (mom experiences our feelings with us as real, painful, and scary)

_____

_____

❖ Structuring (mom helps her child puts feelings in perspective; she helps by talking about feelings as feelings and helps the child develop an observing self)

_____

_____

❖ Confronting (mom helps her child face his out-of-control feelings; she injects reality into his emotions)

_____

_____

❖ Thinking (mom helps us understand our feelings, how we should think about them, and that feelings may not mean what we think they mean)

_____

_____

➤ ➤ ➤ Which of these methods of containing did your mother not use very well? Explain your choice(s).

❖ Soothing

_____

_____

❖ Validating

_____

_____

❖ Structuring

_____

_____

❖ Confronting

_____

_____

❖ Thinking

_____

_____

RESULTS OF FRAGILE MOTHERING

Page 65   Various signs and symptoms can help you confirm your hunch that you may have had a China Doll Mom.

➤ ➤ ➤ *Relational Problems.* Which of the following do you see evidence of in your life? Give specific examples and tell what they suggest about the mothering you received.

___ Caretaking
___ Aggressiveness
___ Withdrawal

_____

_____

_____

_____

➤ ➤ ➤ *Functional Problems.* Of which of the following do you see evidence in your life? Give specific examples and tell what they suggest about the mothering you received.

___ Career snags
___ Life problem-solving
___ Rigid thinking styles

_____
_____
_____
_____

➤ ➤ ➤ *Emotional Problems.* Which of the following do you see evidence of in your life? Give specific examples and tell what they suggest about the mothering you received.

___ Depression
___ Anxiety problems
___ Behavioral problems

_____
_____
_____
_____

NOWADAYS WITH MOM

Page 68   It's difficult to try to relate to a fragile mom who's getting older. Many adult kids are unable to separate the fragility of the declining years from mom's character resistance to taking ownership of her life.

➤ ➤ ➤ Talking with people who have strong moms the same age as your mom can help you assess your situation. Who might offer you both perspective about how to deal with an aging mom and a clear picture of mom's true welfare needs?

_____
_____
_____
_____

➤ ➤ ➤   Taking care of mom in her old age may not be all you struggle with. Do you, for instance, feel obliged to share only "good news" about yourself and your family? Why don't you talk with mom about job struggles or childrearing issues—or yourself?

_____

_____

_____

_____

➤ ➤ ➤   What do you think might happen if you tried to talk to your mother about your relationship with her?

_____

_____

_____

_____

➤ ➤ ➤   How are your siblings dealing with your China Doll Mom? And how are they relating to you as you try to build a healthier relationship with her—or how do you expect them to as you begin to take action?

_____

_____

_____

_____

There is hope for the adult child of a China Doll Mom. You don't have to constantly walk the tightrope of compliance and caretaking. You'll learn about the resolution of this issue in the next chapter.

God, I've learned a lot by looking back at certain scenes from my childhood. I now understand more about why I tend to avoid emotion or why I seem to attract problem people. I also realize that I have work to do when it comes to caring for my mom as she gets older. Please give me people who can offer a realistic perspective and healthy alternatives for helping an aging parent. And please give me the courage to stop walking the tightrope of compliance. Amen.

FIVE ❧

Getting It Together

Marty knew that if he could just empathize with Carol, everything would be all right. But he could not calm down. His anger stayed strong no matter what he tried to do about it. But then Carol moved toward him just to hold and caress him. As she held him, his rage began to disappear, and soft tender connecting feelings began to emerge. He reached out to her.

THE LEARNING CURVE

Page 72   Marty was at a point where true insight takes place—he had moved past experiencing the problem to looking at the problem as a problem. He realized he had a problem with being angry a lot. He saw a pattern and knew it was time to do something about it.

➤➤➤ Have you reached the point of realizing you have a problem and knowing it's time to do something about it? What pattern of behavior did you identify that led you to that realization?

_____

_____

_____

➤➤➤ What happened to help you recognize your pattern and decide to move beyond the symptoms to the root problem?

_____

_____

_____

_____

_____

_____

➤ ➤ ➤ How do you think your China Doll Mom contributed to that pattern?

_____

_____

_____

_____

Marty's China Doll Mom had not contained his feelings and overwhelming internal states, so as an adult he couldn't contain his feelings. He needed to learn to do so in order to move beyond the symptoms and fix the problem.

REMEMBER THE PROBLEMS

Page 72   The real problem is that we need to be restored to mothering. Whatever we failed to receive the first time around, we still need.

➤ ➤ ➤ Identify, if you can, what you failed to receive the first time around. To begin, review the five things—the five jewels—your China Doll Mom was probably unable to provide:

___ Soothing
___ Validating
___ Structuring
___ Confronting
___ Thinking

➤ ➤ ➤ What feelings, impulses, and parts of yourself have you not been able to accept and integrate?

_____

_____

_____

_____

In this chapter, we'll discover what we can do to get the mothering we need, to fix the fragile mother inside.

THE JEWELS

Page 72 When Nicodemus went to Jesus to see if he was truly a teacher from God, Jesus said, "Unless a man is born again, he cannot see the kingdom of God." Nicodemus knew he couldn't be born again through his mother—and neither can we. Nevertheless, we do have to start over, but it can't be with mother.

➤ ➤ ➤ Being restored to mothering comes when we enter a relationship with God through Jesus and then mature through the spiritual-growth process.

❖ If you have already entered a relationship with God, how do you think that relationship will help you be restored to mothering—or how has it helped already? More specifically, what can God do to help you be restored to mothering?

_____

_____

_____

_____

❖ We enter a relationship with God by acknowledging our sinfulness, asking God for forgiveness, recognizing that his forgiveness comes through Jesus' death on the cross and resurrection from the dead, and naming Jesus as our Savior. What obstacles stand in the way of your entering this relationship? With whom can you talk to about those obstacles? About questions you may have regarding a relationship with God?

_____

_____

_____

_____

In the spiritual-growth process, in relationship with God and his people, we find the jewels of mothering. As others share their gifts with us, we receive the mothering we need. As we connect with God and good people, we internalize this mothering.

➤ ➤ ➤ *Soothing*. When others understand our pain, when we hear caring voices, we are soothed.

❖ Who in your life has understood your pain? How did you benefit from being heard?

_____

_____

_____

❖ Who in your life today understands your pain and offers a caring voice?

_____

_____

_____

➤ ➤ ➤ *Validating*. Being validated is being understood and knowing that our experience is real.

❖ Who in your life has validated your feelings? Be specific about a particular incident and tell how you responded to that validation.

_____

_____

_____

❖ Who in your life today understands your pain and offers a caring voice?

_____

_____

_____

➤ ➤ ➤ *Structuring*. After our feelings have been validated, we can understand them and put them in perspective. We can also begin to think about what we are going to do.

❖ Who in your life has helped you see the big picture, remember that God is in control, and begin to formulate plans by listening to you? How did you benefit from this structuring? Be specific.

_____

_____

_____

➤ ➤ ➤ *Confronting.* We need honest friends who will confront us when we are not seeing reality. Their confrontation limits our tendency to blow things out of propor-
tion and scare ourselves to death.

❖ When has someone confronted you? How did you react initially? How did
the confrontation help you?

_____

_____

_____

❖ Who in your life today confronts you when necessary?

_____

_____

_____

➤ ➤ ➤ *Thinking.* We need to think about our thinking. As we observe our feelings and
talk about them, we begin to observe *how* we are thinking in addition to *what* we
are thinking.

❖ As you've talked about your feelings and thoughts, what have you noticed
about your thinking? Have you noticed negative, pessimistic, paranoid, overly
critical, or self-centered thinking? What might be the roots of the thinking
you've identified?

_____

_____

_____

❖ When has recognizing your thinking patterns helped calm you down?
Describe a particular incident.

_____

_____

_____

❖ Who in your life today listens well enough to help you identify your thinking
as you talk?

_____

_____

_____

OUR RESPONSE TO MOTHERING

Page 77 As we saw in the first chapter, not only how we are mothered, but how we respond to mothering is also important.

➤➤➤ If you had difficult mothering, you may fail to respond when mothering is available to you. How have you resisted the mothering available to you?

_____

_____

_____

_____

➤➤➤ What defenses, such as withdrawal, angry control, and compliance, have you relied on?

_____

_____

_____

_____

➤➤➤ Until we take responsibility for our response to mothering, we will remain stuck with the lack of containment we had as a child.

❖ How, if at all, are you resisting the mothering available to you today?

_____

_____

_____

❖ Or are you taking responsibility for your response to that available mothering? Support your answer with specifics.

_____

_____

_____

TASKS

Page 78 If you are serious about responding to the mothering available to you, if you are in fact taking responsibility for your response to mothering, you need to accomplish certain specific tasks.

1. Find a safe place.

➤ ➤ ➤ Questions in the "Jewels" section may have helped you realize whether or not you've found a safe place. What safe place(s) have you found?

___A regular meeting with a wise and understanding friend or two
___An open, relational church that encourages personal growth
___A Bible study where you can process your feelings and experiences
___A support group
___A professional therapy group
___Individual counseling

➤ ➤ ➤ If you haven't found a safe place, which possible safe place will you pursue first?

_____

_____

_____

2. Risk intense emotions.

➤ ➤ ➤ What benefits can come when you allow people into the immediate experience of your overwhelming emotional states?

_____

_____

_____

➤ ➤ ➤ What's keeping you from letting yourself risk intense emotions and internalizing mothering?

_____

_____

_____

3. Respond to empathy and validation.

➤ ➤ ➤ With what statements do you tend to devalue your feelings and dismiss people's words of love and grace? What can you tell yourself to refute those statements and enable yourself to accept empathy and validation?

_____

_____

_____

➤ ➤ ➤ What defensive patterns keep you from receiving and responding? What can you do to break those patterns?

_____

_____

_____

4. Learn to think about feelings and observe yourself.

➤ ➤ ➤ What themes characterize your negative thinking? (If you're not sure, try journaling for a week to see if writing can help you think about and observe your feelings and experiences.)

_____

_____

_____

➤ ➤ ➤ What positive self-talk will you use to counter your involuntary negative thoughts? Write out some specific statements here.

_____

_____

_____

5. Develop action plans.

➤ ➤ ➤ From which of these possible action steps could you benefit?

____ Building more support
____ Reading certain books or articles

___ Doing some homework assignments
___ Studying a portion of the Bible
___ Confronting someone

➤ ➤ ➤ Choose one step now and develop a specific plan and some attainable goals.

_____

_____

_____

_____

6. Give empathy to and validate others.

➤ ➤ ➤ When has loving others and helping them moved you out of self-centeredness? Be specific.

_____

_____

_____

➤ ➤ ➤ In the incident you just referred to, what did you learn about emotions, catastrophizing, and/or negative thinking? How did—or could—those lessons help you deal with your own overwhelming emotions and negative thoughts?

_____

_____

_____

Receiving what we missed out on the first time around is the bedrock of growth, and these six tasks can help you lay that foundation.

DEALING WITH YOUR CHINA DOLL MOM OF THE PAST

`Page 80` What you did receive the first time around may be hurtful. If it was, you need to deal with it.

➤ ➤ ➤ How is your mother still in your head? What thought patterns, for instance, are an internalization of her voice?

_____

_____

_____

_____

➤ ➤ ➤ Present feelings about past experiences and people can get in the way of present feelings toward present people. What feelings and responses to unresolved relationships and experiences in the past are you carrying around in the present?

_____

_____

_____

_____

If we want to be finished with the mother of the past, we must go through the process of forgiveness and reconciliation. In doing this, we find incredible freedom and love. Let's look at what it takes to forgive the China Doll Mom.

FIND A SAFE ISLAND

Page 80   Getting finished with our mother from yesterday involves letting go of hurts and whatever else may be dragging us down.

➤ ➤ ➤ What hurts and other emotions (sadness, anger, suspiciousness, bitterness) from the past may be dragging you down? Be specific.

_____

_____

_____

_____

➤ ➤ ➤ What problems with your mother do you need to forgive and grieve so that you can free up space and energy for other attachments?

_____

_____

_____

_____

BECOME AWARE

Page 81 Often, our patterns of relating in the present really belong to our relationship with our mother. Dynamics and patterns that were standard procedure in our experience of her, as well as the ways that we responded, will often still be very much alive when we are adults.

➤ ➤ ➤ Awareness, in a mothering context, is consciousness of the automatic patterns that belong specifically to our relationship with our mother. If you had a China Doll Mom, what patterns of relating did you develop in response to her fragility?

___ Withdrawal

___ Denial of feelings or needs for fear of overwhelming others

___ _____

➤ ➤ ➤ If you work on remembering the patterns and experiences, they will lose some of their power in the present and become less operative.

❖ How can your support people help you take this step?

_____

_____

_____

_____

❖ What healthy truths can you use to respond to the automatic mom voice in your head? Be specific.

_____

_____

_____

_____

HOW DO YOU FEEL?

Page 82 As we become connected and begin to feel safe, and as we look realistically at the way mother really was, we become aware of certain feelings we have about her. Becoming aware of these feelings is the beginning of working through the pain that her fragility caused.

➤ ➤ ➤ Which of the following aspects of grief work have you started? Comment on the progress you're making.

___ Becoming aware of your feelings
___ Expressing your feelings
___ Understanding your feelings
___ Letting yourself be comforted
___ Letting go of your feelings

_____

_____

_____

➤ ➤ ➤ Are anger, sadness, or other feelings still unresolved in your relationship with your mom? Try to put words to those feelings and/or explain the reasons for any anger or sadness you're feeling.

_____

_____

_____

➤ ➤ ➤ What safe person can you talk to about the feelings you just described? Talking to him/her will help you process those feelings so you aren't carrying them around in the present.

_____

_____

_____

_____

FORGIVING

Page 82   To forgive means to "cancel a debt." To forgive mom means making peace
with her—coming to a place where she no longer "owes" us.

➤ ➤ ➤ Where are you in the process of forgiveness?

___ Understanding what happened
___ Processing feelings of anger or sadness
___ Learning to let those feelings go

➤ ➤ ➤ Remind yourself of the importance of forgiveness by answering the question
"Why is forgiveness good for you?" Put differently, how will you benefit from forgiving mom?

_____

_____

_____

_____

DEALING WITH MOTHER TODAY

Page 83   So what about mom today? What are you going to do with her in the area
of containment?

➤ ➤ ➤ Janet learned to not take parts of her that needed soothing and containing to her
China Doll Mom. She could take other parts to her, but not those. How does
your mom react to your needs for soothing?

_____

_____

_____

➤ ➤ ➤ Who can offer you the soothing and containing you need?

_____

_____

_____

➤ ➤ ➤ What aspects of your life are you comfortable and safe sharing with your mother? Save those for her and let others provide you the soothing and containing you need.

_____

_____

_____

TALK ABOUT THE ISSUE

Page 84
If your mother has difficulty relating in a particular area and you want to work it out, you'll need to discuss that difficult area with her.

➤ ➤ ➤ Is talking about the issue a possibility for you and your mom? Why or why not? (If it's not, move on to "Not So Hopeful Situations.")

_____

_____

_____

➤ ➤ ➤ If so, review the coaching you might offer mom (p. 84). What will you say to make this message your own? With whom will you practice sharing this message? When will you talk to mom?

_____

_____

_____

Many moms respond wonderfully to a little coaching. If yours does, you could be on the way to a whole new era with your mother. Your support relationships will still meet your need for containment, but you and mom can have a mutually satisfying relationship.

NOT SO HOPEFUL SITUATIONS

Page 85
Some moms are either unable or unwilling to respond to their adult child's request for a deeper friendship. If this is true of your mother, we suggest the following.

1. Get safety somewhere.

➤ ➤ ➤ As we've asked before, where do you find safety? Describe your support system.

_____

_____

_____

➤ ➤ ➤ Which tasks mentioned earlier (see workbook pages 52–54) are you tackling in order to get what you need in the way of containment and soothing?

_____

_____

_____

2. Set some limits—on yourself and with her.

➤ ➤ ➤ What limits will you set for yourself in these areas? Be specific.

Topics of conversation
Your vulnerability
Your exposure to her
Your wishes to be understood by her

_____

_____

_____

_____

➤ ➤ ➤ Setting limits with mother may involve saying "That's just Mom" when she hurts you once again, or it may mean actually telling her, "Mom, if you continue to criticize, then I'll have to stop talking. Would you like to talk about something else?" What are your thoughts on the viability of these solutions? When will you start setting limits with mom using one of these approaches?

_____

_____

_____

_____

3. Relate where she can.

➤ ➤ ➤ What did you learn from Stan's experience?

_____

_____

_____

_____

➤ ➤ ➤ What are one or two specific areas you can safely relate to mom about?

_____

_____

_____

_____

4. Love her in your best way.

➤ ➤ ➤ How does your China Doll Mom deal with neediness: Does she attack neediness or is she destroyed by it?

_____

_____

_____

_____

➤ ➤ ➤ Even though mom is unable to share vulnerably to promote intimacy, she still yearns to be liked and valued. What can you do to show her you value her? Be specific. Choose one idea to act on this week.

_____

_____

_____

_____

CONCLUSION

Page 87

If you had a fragile mother, you are still in need of containment. You need soothing and structuring, and you can get this from other people in your life and from God. They are there to help, but you have to ask.

➤ ➤ ➤ Who can you ask—or who are you asking—for soothing and structuring?

_____

_____

_____

_____

➤ ➤ ➤ Once you place yourself in good mothering relationships, you have to learn to receive what is given. Evaluate your ability to receive. You might, for instance, cite examples of when you have let yourself be soothed. Or you might think through the "mom in the head" talk that has kept you from receiving.

_____

_____

_____

_____

➤ ➤ ➤ Forgive your mom for what she could not do. Where are you in that process?

_____

_____

_____

_____

➤ ➤ ➤ Finally, work out the relationship that you have with her now. What limits are you setting? What topics and activities are safe? How are you loving her in your best way?

_____

_____

_____

_____

As you work to build a healthier relationship with your China Doll Mom, forgive her for what she could not do. In this kind of love, you both may find something very rewarding.

God, it's hard for me to ask for anything—from you or from people. But I don't have anything to lose right now. So please help me. Teach me how to contain and structure my feelings by giving me people to listen to me and by listening to me yourself. Then, God, help me to receive what you and those others have to offer and help me to forgive my mom. Amen.

SIX ❧

The Controlling Mom

From the day her daughter Ali was born, Nancy imagined a wonderful future for her—music lessons, the prom, graduation, college, and a wedding. But difficulties became apparent early on and continued through Ali's adolescence and young adulthood. The two developed a love/hate relationship, and both continued to feel hurt by the other. When Ali chose not to go to college, Nancy felt she had failed as a mother and that Ali had let her down. In turn, Ali felt lost, estranged from her mother, and confused about what to do with the rest of her life.

➤ ➤ ➤ What scenes—if any—from your own childhood does the story of Nancy and Ali's relationship (pp. 89–90) call to mind? Be specific about points of conflict and how you and mom handled them.

_____

_____

_____

_____

THE NEED TO BE ONE'S OWN PERSON

Page 90   It's absolutely important that a mother provide a close nurturing relationship for her child. After that connection occurs, the next big task of mothering is to assist the child in becoming an individual in his own right. Maintaining connection and fostering separateness are the challenges of mothering. Let's look at four tasks moms must complete to meet these challenges for their children.

64

➤ ➤ ➤ Allow and foster independence and assertion of will, intentionality, and separateness.

❖ What did your mom do to foster your independence? Be specific.

_____

_____

_____

_____

❖ How did mom react when you asserted your will? What particular incidents stand out in your mind as you consider this question?

_____

_____

_____

_____

❖ To what degree was your mom able to let you have a life of your own, separate and distinct from her? Explain.

_____

_____

_____

_____

_____

_____

If a mother is unable to let her child have a life of his own, the child will be broken, or mother and child will battle until someone wins.

➤ ➤ ➤ Allow and foster individual identity and differences.

❖ What limits did mom set on your self-expression? On your choices about clothes, friends, food, and music?

_____

_____

_____

❖ How did mom respond to choices you made that wouldn't have been her choices for you?

_____

_____

_____

❖ Your sense of identity today offers a clue as to how much freedom your mom allowed you to be different. Do you feel basically okay or not okay? Did you fight to have your own identity as you were growing up or did you give in passively to not having one at all?

_____

_____

_____

Part of the mother's task is to set boundaries. She enforces limits and allows freedom at the same time. But she must resist enforcing limits only to keep her child from being different from her.

➤ ➤ ➤ Discipline poor choices, behaviors, and attitudes and set limits.

❖ When you think of your growing-up years, do you remember being disciplined or punished? Explain by answering the following questions. What boundaries and limits did your mom set? Did she consistently enforce the consequences for violating those limits and values? Was discipline dad's job? Was mom an enabler?

_____

_____

_____

❖ Your ability to say no to yourself may suggest how well mom said no to you. Evaluate your self-control. Do you say no to yourself when you need to, or is saying no to yourself a problem either across the board or in specific areas? Explain.

_____

_____

_____

❖ Are you willing and able to take responsibility for yourself—for your feelings, choices, behaviors, and attitudes? Or do you more easily and readily blame circumstances or people for problems in your life? What do your answers to these questions suggest about your mother's ability to discipline your choices, behaviors, and attitudes?

_____

_____

_____

_____

The good-enough mother allows freedom, sets limits, and enforces the rules with consequences. Done lovingly, these things teach children that freedom and responsibility go hand in hand. Children also learn what it means to own and take responsibility for their feelings, choices, behaviors, and attitudes. In doing so, they learn self-control.

➤ ➤ ➤ Frustrate the child's wish to avoid independence and separateness. The child wants independence and fights it at the same time.

❖ What do you remember about experiencing this struggle between wanting independence and fighting it when you were growing up? Be specific.

_____

_____

_____

_____

_____

❖ How well did you internalize the ability to say no to your own regressive wishes to be taken care of? Answer that question by sharing an incident that shows how you dealt with the desire (however fleeting or well-rooted) to bail out of adult responsibilities.

_____

_____

_____

_____

Like the mother bird who says, "Long enough in the nest," the good-enough mother says "long enough" at every stage of development and helps her child move to the next one.

➤ ➤ ➤   The benefits of having a mother who does these important mothering tasks well are summarized on pages 96–97 of the text.

❖   What do you see about yourself as you look in the mirror that is provided by this description of children who have had a good-enough mom?

_____

_____

_____

_____

❖   Do you see areas for growth? Name them.

_____

_____

_____

_____

Now consider what might have kept you from receiving the benefits of being allowed separateness and will, and of being raised with limits and discipline.

WHAT GETS IN THE WAY?

Page 97   If mom has a problem with her child's budding independence, separating can be a difficult process for both. Mothers can attack their child's independence in many ways.

➤ ➤ ➤   When you read of Jeri's mother's response to the spring vacation issue, did any of your own growing-up experiences come to mind? If so, describe them.

_____

_____

_____

_____

➤ ➤ ➤ Of the following common ways moms attack their child's independence, which did you encounter when you were growing up?

___ Guilt ("You are destroying me by being independent.")
___ Abandonment and withdrawal of love ("I don't love you if you separate.")
___ Attack and anger ("Your individuality is my enemy, and I will destroy it.")
___ Lack of structure (Without love to move away from and a structure to move against, a child cannot build secure autonomy.)

➤ ➤ ➤ What consequences of the guilt, anger, abandonment, and/or lack of structure are you dealing with today?

_____

_____

_____

The enemies of finding our true identity are guilt, anger, abandonment, and lack of structure. The friends are freedom, love, and responsibility.

THE RESULTS OF A CONTROLLING MOM

Page 99

In the same way that detached and fragile mothering leave the child with problems later in life, so does mothering that does not foster ownership, responsibility, and identity.

➤ ➤ ➤ *Relational Problems.* Which of these problems do you experience? (See descriptions on pp. 100–101.)

___ Inability to say no
___ Control issues (using anger, guilt, manipulation, withdrawal of love, and anger to control people)
___ Fear of intimacy and commitment
___ Codependency (not allowing the ones you love to be responsible for their own problems, feelings, attitudes, behaviors, and choices)

➤ ➤ ➤ *Functional Problems.* Which of the following are problems for you? (See descriptions on pp. 101–3.)

___ Disorganization (lack of organization of desires, goals, time, and efforts)
___ Identity and talents ("can't find my niche" syndrome; not knowing what you want to do, what you like and dislike, what your talents and abilities are)

___ Delay of gratification

___ Irresponsibility

➤➤➤ *Emotional Problems.* Which of the following do you deal with? (See descriptions on pp. 103–5.)

___ Depression

___ Feelings of powerlessness and hopelessness

___ Addictions and impulse problems

___ Isolation

___ Anxiety states and panic attacks

___ Blaming

We have seen how the Controlling Mom affects her child's growing up. The sad reality is that these patterns often continue when the adult child is out on his own.

WHAT IT LOOKS LIKE NOW

Page 105

We've seen people in their twenties to people in their seventies still struggling to take ownership of their lives, a task that they should have completed as young adults. Let's look at a few of the ways that adults continue that pattern after they leave home.

➤➤➤ "She won't let me."

❖ What did you learn from the forty-one-year-old woman's complaint that her mother wouldn't let her choose her own career?

_____

_____

_____

❖ In what area of your life (if any) are you choosing to let your mom control you? Where are you choosing to try to keep her happy rather than choosing what you think is right for you?

_____

_____

_____

➤ ➤ ➤ "Just a little to get me through the end of the month."

❖   What, if anything, do you see about yourself in Joe's and Steve's experiences?

_____

_____

_____

❖   Where is mom bailing you out or at least helping you do a little better than you could do on your own?

_____

_____

_____

❖   Where are you still leaning on mom so you don't have to experience the consequences of life? What would you learn from experiencing those consequences?

_____

_____

_____

Good mothering provides a relationship secure in love as well as steadfast in the push toward independence and responsibility; it manifests itself in the child's ability to take ownership of his life. A well-mothered person has a strong identity, but he can relate in a way that is responsible and rewarding to others. If you're not there yet, learn in the next chapter how to repair the problems your Controlling Mom may have caused you and how to deal responsibly with her now that you are an adult.

God, all this talk about independence from mom and assertion of will, intentionality, and separateness has me thinking about what I've missed out on. I'm sensing that I don't take responsibility for myself the way I should because I haven't really had to do that. Or, I take too much responsibility for others.

And I realize I'm dealing with guilt, anger, abandonment, and/or lack of structure today. I'm relieved to understand a little more about where certain relational, functional, and emotional problems come from, but I'm not exactly sure where to go from here. Please provide what I need—and be with me as I figure it out. Amen.

SEVEN ∿

Becoming Your Own Person

The very purpose of mothering is to enable a child to become independent of mom. This chapter provides steps for repair when that purpose isn't realized.

➤ ➤ ➤ If you had a Controlling Mom, you've most likely experienced problems in separation, autonomy, and individuation—becoming your own person. Describe your attempt to become your own person and the degree of success you have experienced up to this point.

_____

_____

_____

_____

Here you'll find ways to become the you that God intended you to be. Before we go through the necessary steps, let's clarify the real problem.

WHAT AND WHO IS THE PROBLEM AGAIN?

Page 109   The Controlling Mom may be the hardest mother type to perceive accurately and realistically.

➤ ➤ ➤ The bottom-line issues and dynamics in a relationship with a Controlling Mom are often difficult to identify because of two tendencies.

❖ First, people with a Controlling Mom tend to see her as the solution. Second, people with a Controlling Mom tend to see her as the problem. Which has been your tendency?

_____

_____

_____

❖ Explain how an undeveloped independence or the need to develop one's identity, autonomy, and ability to set boundaries can be the real issues behind these two tendencies.

_____

_____

_____

Your Controlling Mom and your present relational, functional, emotional, and spiritual struggles may be connected. And once you've owned the problem, you will be ready to develop your remothering relationships.

PEOPLE TO HELP ME BECOME ME

Page 110

Forming your separate identity involves differentiating yourself from others. You learn this from many experiences of saying no, disagreeing with other people's opinions, and confronting others.

➤ ➤ ➤ Your need to become your own person is tied up in the need to differentiate yourself from others. What does or could "differentiating yourself from others" look like in your day-to-day life? Be specific about opportunities you have to say no, to disagree with other people's opinions, and to confront others.

_____

_____

_____

_____

_____

> ➤ ➤ ➤ Your supportive people (and not everyone is right for the task) need to commit themselves to you in this process of differentiating yourself from others. They also need the qualities listed below. Next to each write why it is important to your remothering.

❖ The ability to be intimate

_____

_____

❖ The willingness to stay connected to you even in conflict

_____

_____

❖ Honesty

_____

_____

❖ The ability to encourage you to take risks in asserting yourself

_____

_____

❖ Process-oriented: able and willing to give you time to grow

_____

_____

THE NEEDS OF BECOMING YOUR OWN PERSON

Page 112 You need to complete certain basic tasks with the help of your remothering people to "grow yourself up." They break down into several categories.

➤ ➤ ➤ Develop a separate will and the ability to decide what you love and don't love, like and don't like, want and don't want.

❖ Explain what is meant by "We can't really know who we are until we know who we aren't."

_____

_____

_____

❖ Review Corinne's experience. What will you do this week to take ownership of your "no" muscle?

_____

_____

_____

➤ ➤ ➤ Create an identity.

❖ At this point, what interests, talents, abilities, or personality traits can you identify that make you uniquely you?

_____

_____

_____

❖ What encouragement do you find in Jeff's story? What parts of yourself have lain dormant? Which area will you first work to develop?

_____

_____

_____

➤ ➤ ➤ Live within limits.

❖ Why is it important for people to experience the consequences of their poor choices?

_____

_____

_____

❖ What did you learn from Danielle's experience? In what area(s) of your life have you been protected from the consequences of poor decisions? What changes might happen in you and/or how you live once you have to face those consequences?

_____

_____

_____

➤ ➤ ➤ Deal with dependency.

❖ Explain the difference between love and caretaking. How can remothering help you learn to say no to your wish to be parented, to be taken care of rather than to take responsibility for yourself?

_____

_____

_____

❖ How did wishes for caretaking interfere with Burt's career? How is the wish for caretaking interfering with your life?

_____

_____

_____

SKILLS IN BECOMING YOU

Page 117

If you're serious about developing the separate identity you were created to be, you must take responsibility for the process. The following steps will help.

➤ ➤ ➤ Know your defining traits.

❖ If you haven't done so already, answer the questions below. Afterward note what you specifically identified about yourself for the first time.

___ Am I more extroverted or introverted?

___ Am I more task-oriented or relationship-oriented?

___ Am I more active or passive?

___ What aspects of my family background do I agree with?

___ What aspects aren't me?

___ What do I like in my best friends?

___ What do I dislike in my best friends?

___ What are my strengths?

___ What are my weaknesses?

___ What situations make me angry?

_____

_____

_____

_____

_____

❖ Ask your remothering people about which of the character traits listed define you and which don't. See how their answers correspond with your own view of yourself.

_____

_____

_____

➤➤➤ Develop your "no" muscle.

❖ What evidence do you have that indicates that your "yes" muscle is overdeveloped? When has that muscle worked even when you inwardly disagree?

_____

_____

_____

❖ Who will you take to a used-car lot (or its equivalent) to practice saying no? When will you go?

_____

_____

_____

➤➤➤ Deal with the victim role.

❖ Why do some people define themselves as a victim and create an identity out of an event? What hard work do they avoid when they do so?

_____

_____

_____

❖ Are you defining yourself as a victim and creating an identity out of an event? Comment on the wisdom of the woman who said, "I can't change my past. It's part of me. But I don't want my past to determine my future. If I do, the

people who hurt me are in charge again." What will you do to move away
from a victim mentality?

_____

_____

_____

➤ ➤ ➤ Develop proactivity.

❖ Is it easier for you to react or to take initiative? Give an example or two supporting your answer.

_____

_____

_____

❖ What will you do this week to take the initiative in social plans? What will you
do this week to get your relational needs met rather than waiting and hoping
someone will notice you are sad or struggling?

_____

_____

_____

➤ ➤ ➤ Set boundaries.

❖ In what aspect of your life are you currently being unclear about your boundaries? In what relationship or situation do you need to state your limits and
then keep the consequences if your boundaries aren't honored?

_____

_____

_____

❖ What role did Alicia's supportive friends play in her attempt to set boundaries with Stuart? What will you ask your support group to help you do to establish boundaries in an area you just identified?

_____

_____

_____

➤ ➤ ➤ Respect others' boundaries.

❖ Where are you not respecting the boundaries of someone in your life?

_____

_____

_____

❖ When he had to cancel a much-anticipated fishing trip, Chase said to his disappointed friend, "I'm not doing this *against you*. I'm doing it *for me*." When have you taken personally a no that came when someone maintained his/her boundaries? What will you do to show your support of a person's no the next time that happens?

_____

_____

_____

RE-RELATING TO MOM

Page 121   As you become more defined, separate, and independent, you will need to reconfigure your connection with mom. You want, as much as possible, to bring your "me" to the "we" of the relationship. Here are some of the things you can do to move this process along.

➤ ➤ ➤ Become aware of mom's struggle.

❖ How has your mother been hurt in the area of boundaries? Explain—or find out.

_____

_____

_____

❖ How did or will this understanding help you re-relate to mom?

_____

_____

_____

➤➤➤ Introduce mom to the new "you."

❖ What about the new "you" would you like to introduce to mom? What discoveries about your character traits, attributes, likes, and dislikes would you like to tell her about?

_____

_____

_____

_____

❖ What reaction to your sharing do you expect? How will you cope with that? When will you introduce yourself to mom?

_____

_____

_____

_____

➤➤➤ Set necessary limits.

❖ What new ground rules for relating to mom are appropriate now? The four suggestions listed on pages 121–22 might give you some ideas.

_____

_____

_____

_____

❖ If your remothering friends feel that you're ready for this step, what will you say to mom about setting new limits in your relationship?

_____

_____

_____

_____

➤ ➤ ➤ Help mom with her own limits.

❖ Does mom have difficulty being an individual in her own life? How well does she do following through on boundaries and consequences? Support your answers with some specifics.

_____

_____

_____

_____

❖ What would you like to do to help your mom learn what you've learned about boundaries? Remember—you're not trying to parent your parent!

_____

_____

_____

HOW IT COULD BE

Page 123
As you continue becoming a separate person in your own relationships, you will also see positive changes in your attachment to mom.

➤ ➤ ➤ What encouragement did you find in the story of Julia and her mom? What things that Julia did might work in your relationship with your mom?

_____

_____

_____

_____

➤ ➤ ➤ When two people create good space between them, they create room for loving and intimate feelings.

❖ When have you experienced good space in a relationship? Be specific about the effort and the benefits involved.

_____

_____

❖ What will you do to try to create good space in your relationship with mom?
   If mom's willing and able to look at herself, you may have gained a friend. If
   not, you've done your part to improve the relationship, and you may have to
   leave it at that.

_____

_____

_____

It's not easy, but when mother and adult child can move into appreciation of each
other's independence, they can find that closeness they've longed for with one
another.

*God, I have a lot of work to do. First, help me to understand the real problem and
to take responsibility for myself where I need to. Then, as I work on differentiating myself from others, show me clearly who you made me to be. Give me the
courage and ability to develop the skills I need to become that person. And then
help me work on re-relating to mom. Amen.*

EIGHT ～

The Trophy Mom

As far back as he could remember, Dan had felt that his mother, Liz, was proud of him; she would bask in the glow of her son's achievements. Other times, however, she needed the praise directly for herself—and that need for admiration seemed to happen more at dinnertime, when she had a captive audience. The family's "Point Man" strategy enabled them to survive dinners without hurting Liz's feelings. Part of Dan needed his mom's admiration, but it was hard to listen to her talk in great detail about herself with full embellishments and dramatic pauses.

➤ ➤ ➤ What scenes or feelings from your own childhood does this story call to mind? Be specific about your mom's pride in you and her pride in herself.

_____

_____

_____

_____

OUR NEED FOR ACCEPTANCE

Page 127   Dan's relationship with Liz illustrates the basic human need to be accepted in all our parts. We need a place where we can be ourselves, just as we are.

➤ ➤ ➤ When we are accepted, we learn that love is the antidote to badness.

❖ When has love helped you accept badness in the world, in other people, or, most importantly for this discussion, in yourself?

_____

_____

_____

❖ How does a mom's acceptance help her child face reality?

_____

_____

_____

➤ ➤ ➤ Acceptance and approval are two different things.

❖ Explain the difference between acceptance and approval.

_____

_____

_____

❖ What does a good-enough mom accept in her child but not approve of? What did your mom accept but not approve of? Did her (too) generous approval lead to some perfectionistic ideals with which you still measure yourself? If so, be specific about what those ideals are.

_____

_____

_____

A mom's healthy acceptance of her child limits his grandiose self and helps the child give up idealistic demands on himself and others. This process prepares the child to enter adult life with sound judgment about his strengths and weaknesses, positives and negatives, goods and bads.

PARTS THAT NEED ACCEPTANCE

`Page 129` Several parts of a child need acceptance.

➤ ➤ ➤ Identify one or two traits in each of the following categories that need acceptance.

❖ Your weak parts

_____

❖ Your negative parts

_____

❖   Your mediocre parts

_____

❖   The parts your mom doesn't like

_____

❖   Your bad parts

_____

➤ ➤ ➤ What do you remember about your mom's responses to the following:

❖   Your weak parts

_____

_____

❖   Your negative parts

_____

_____

❖   Your mediocre parts

_____

_____

❖   The parts your mom doesn't like

_____

_____

❖   Your bad parts

_____

_____

➤ ➤ ➤ What does your ability or inability to identify these parts of you that need acceptance show about perfectionistic ideals you have for yourself? From your memory
of mom's reaction to these parts of you, what conclusions do you draw about
yourself? About her?

_____

_____

_____

OUR NEED FOR INTEGRATION

Page 130 Children need someone who can relate to both their feelings of love and their feelings of hate about themselves and the world. They desperately need mom to connect to their hatred of her as well as their loving feelings for her.

➤ ➤ ➤ When mom can deal with both kinds of feelings in her child, the two parts begin to integrate. The child's love is tempered with reality and the hatred is tempered with closeness. The child develops the ability to be ambivalent.

❖ Are you able to be ambivalent? In what relationships have you felt both love and hate?

_____

_____

_____

❖ Or do love and hate remain separated for you? Do you see people as either good guys or bad guys? How realistic or helpful is this when it comes to relationships?

_____

_____

_____

❖ What evidence can you point to that you see yourself as either good or bad as well?

_____

_____

_____

➤ ➤ ➤ Jean said, "Stop being negative. You need to be more positive."

❖ Did your mom say things like this? Was mom more comfortable with the "ups" of your world and unwilling to acknowledge the "down" parts? Give an example.

_____

_____

_____

_____

❖ How do you react to the "downs" in your world and your friends' worlds?

_____

_____

_____

_____

❖ What benefits come from acknowledging both the "down" parts of the world and of people as well as the "ups"?

_____

_____

_____

_____

OUR NEED FOR FORGIVENESS

Page 131 Many of a child's parts need a mom's forgiveness. When that forgiveness is extended, children learn that they can hurt others and still be connected through forgiveness.

➤ ➤ ➤ What did your mom model about the forgiveness process?

_____

_____

_____

➤ ➤ ➤ What did mom do to help you learn to forgive others for their transgressions?

_____

_____

_____

_____

OUR NEED TO LEARN TO GRIEVE

Page 131   To deal with and resolve loss, badness, and failure, children need to learn to grieve. Grief is the process of letting go of that which we cannot keep.

➤ ➤ ➤ How did your mom respond to the disappointments in your life? Tell of a time when she devalued your loss or when she wept when you wept. How did you feel when she responded as she did?

_____

_____

_____

_____

➤ ➤ ➤ What did you learn about grief from mom?

_____

_____

_____

_____

REAL ME AND IDEAL ME

Page 132   We all have two "me's," or emotional pictures of ourselves, in our heads. One is the *real me*—the self that actually is. The other is the *ideal me*—the person we would like to be.

➤ ➤ ➤ Did mom love the real you more than the ideal you? Explain why you answered as you did.

_____

_____

_____

_____

➤ ➤ ➤ When a mother makes the fatal mistake of loving the ideal over the real, of pre-
ferring the child who "should be," the child does the same himself. Have you
tried—or are you still trying—to be perfect and "have it all together" to keep
people close and involved? Comment on the burden you're carrying and how you
feel about carrying it.

_____

_____

_____

_____

BEING "GOOD ENOUGH"

Page 133   Our real self needs also to be a *good-enough self*.

➤ ➤ ➤ Explain how a mother's love can lay to rest the "Am I good or bad?" issue for her
child.

_____

_____

_____

_____

➤ ➤ ➤ As we respond to our mother's acceptance of all our parts, we develop a sense
that, because of that love, we feel "good enough." Do you feel "good enough"?
If not, to whom are you turning to receive the acceptance you need?

_____

_____

_____

_____

GOOD SHAME

Page 133
"Good shame" is that particular sense of shame that makes us aware of our failure to be the person we'd like to be. Toxic shame is what we experience when we feel our badness is too bad to be loved.

➤ ➤ ➤ Have you known more good shame or toxic shame in your life? Give an example of how you typically experience one kind of shame or the other.

_____

_____

_____

_____

➤ ➤ ➤ What can a mom do to detoxify the bad shame and show her child how to experience the effects of good shame? If necessary, to whom can you turn to learn how to do this for yourself?

_____

_____

_____

_____

ADMIRATION VS. LOVE

Page 133
Children need to learn to distinguish between admiration and love. These may seem the same, but they are quite different.

➤ ➤ ➤ Explain the difference between admiration and love.

_____

_____

_____

➤ ➤ ➤ How realistic is your view of yourself? Put differently, are you immune to the seductions of flattery and able to see your negative traits? Based on your answers

to these questions, consider how realistic a view of you your mom had and what
you learned from that view.

_____

_____

_____

_____

THE TWO BREAKDOWNS IN ACCEPTANCE

Page 134 When mom can't accept and deal with the "bad" parts of her child, she
uses one of two different approaches, both of which break down the child's
ability to deal with, forgive, and integrate the good and bad parts.

➤ ➤ ➤ Review the discussions of denial and judgment (pp. 134–35). How did mom respond to your "bad" parts? Did you encounter denial (either active or passive) or
judgment from her? Support your answer with some specifics.

_____

_____

_____

_____

➤ ➤ ➤ What do you feel when you are assertive, make mistakes, or disagree with someone? If self-hatred emerges, what does it tell you about lessons you learned growing up?

_____

_____

_____

RESULTS OF "TROPHY" MOTHERING

Page 135 If you had a Trophy Mom, you may be experiencing some of the following symptoms.

➤ ➤ ➤ *Relational Signs.* Which of these characterize your behavior? (See descriptions on pp. 135–37.)

___Performing for others

___"Appreciate me now and avoid the rush" (narcissism: self-centeredness, needing to be treated as special rather than as simply unique)

___"The Human Mirror" (affirming the grandiose self and denying the imperfect self in other people)

➤ ➤ ➤ *Functional Signs.* Which of these signs do you exhibit? (See descriptions on pp. 137–38.)

___Perfectionism

___When work is not a stage (when expectations of praise and mirroring are not met in the workplace)

___Hiding failure

➤ ➤ ➤ *Emotional Signs.* Which of these signs do you deal with? (See descriptions on pp. 138–39.)

___Depression

___Anxiety, shame, and guilt

___Compulsions and addictions

➤ ➤ ➤ *Spiritual Signs.* (See description on p. 139.) Evaluate how easy or difficult it is for you to feel close to and safe with God. What does the struggle (if it is one) suggest about your sense of badness?

_____

_____

_____

_____

NOWADAYS WITH MOM

Page 139   As the child of a Trophy Mother grows up, mother may still expect her little one to "make me proud," and the adult child may still strive to please her.

➤ ➤ ➤ Are you still trying to please mom in any areas of your life? Which ones?

_____

_____

_____

_____

➤ ➤ ➤ When have you felt betrayed by your Trophy Mom? What real-life failure or struggle of yours was she unable to ignore and excuse? How did she make her disappointment known and how did you respond?

_____

_____

_____

_____

_____

_____

_____

If you had a Trophy Mom, the next chapter will show you the steps to repair the problems, as well as complete what was left unfinished in your own mothering.

God, I'm seeing how I've never felt or been totally accepted by my mom and why I struggle to accept the weak, the negative, the mediocre, and the bad parts of me. I can also see why I'm not so sure you'll totally accept me. But I know I need much that you can offer—your forgiveness, your help—as I learn to grieve, as I gain freedom from toxic shame, and as I begin to overcome those results of trophy mothering. Help me to receive what you and the remothering people in my life can offer me. Amen.

NINE ∼

Getting Real

It was a moment of change for Cliff. His confession of his longtime struggle, of his inability to break his addiction to pornography, was drawing group members closer to him. Slowly he raised his head and checked out the group one by one. His eyes moved from person to person, and a transformation took place as he saw their compassion and lack of condemnation. The power of isolation was broken, and Cliff saw that he did not have to be perfect to be loved.

➤ ➤ ➤ When did you realize—perhaps for the first time—that you do not have to be perfect to be loved? Describe that moment. If you haven't ever experienced that, imagine what freedom you would find. When will you let those benefits outweigh the risk involved in opening up?

_____

_____

_____

_____

_____

➤ ➤ ➤ Those with Trophy Moms have a split inside their personalities. The "good self" on the outside tries to live up to the requirements of being a "trophy," and the "bad self" on the inside either tries to hide or finds a way to act out. With whom have you brought or can you bring your "badness into the light"? How has or how could that help you accept and integrate your inadequacies?

_____

_____

_____

_____

In this chapter, we will look at how to repair trophy mothering.

THE DEATH NO ONE WANTS TO EXPERIENCE

Page 142   We have lost Paradise, and the door to the garden, where things are perfect, is guarded by cherubim with a flaming sword. We are unable to enter
perfection. We are unable to be perfect, to have perfect people in our
lives, and to experience a perfect world.

➤ ➤ ➤   Oh, but how we try with makeup, plastic surgery, small white lies, image management, material possessions, achievement, membership in the right groups,
clubs, or churches . . .

❖   What have you done to try to be perfect?

_____

_____

_____

_____

❖   What blows of the sword have you received? (The previous chapter helped
you identify such blows as depression, the inability to function under the demands of perfectionism, and relationship problems.)

_____

_____

_____

_____

➤ ➤ ➤   The question of achieving the ideal me is a dead issue. But the funeral is still
ahead. Let's get to it.

❖   What do you find hardest to accept about yourself?

_____

_____

_____

_____

❖ What feelings did you have as you answered the previous question?

_____

_____

_____

_____

❖ If you felt sadness, that sadness was the funeral. Explain what you were burying.

_____

_____

_____

_____

Acknowledging that our attempts at perfection aren't working—realizing that we can never be perfect no matter how hard we try—can be really depressing. But relief comes when we recognize that we are not alone in our struggles, that we live in a world of other imperfect people. We can in fact find comfort—and more—from a community of imperfect people. These people who accept who we are and love us into who we need to be will help heal the hurts and enable us to get past the problem of inadequate mothering.

➤ ➤ ➤ If we did not get good enough mothering from mom, we must get it from others. Who among your friends or support group offers you these traits of a true friend? Write down the names or initials of specific people.

❖ Humility (They have acknowledged their own imperfections and no longer demand perfection from themselves.)

_____

❖ Absence of condemnation (They are able to avoid making you feel worse or unacceptable for who you are.)

_____

❖ Absence of denial (They are able to face the reality of your badness, weakness, and imperfection.)

_____

❖ Ability to confront (They possess the courage to tell you what they see.)

_____

❖ Acceptance (They embrace and love you where you are.)

_____

➤ ➤ ➤ As you consider your friends and circle of support, ask yourself whether you've chosen people who have the same demands for perfection as your mom had or people who are too comfortable with their imperfections and are unable to confront you with problems you need to look at.

_____

_____

_____

_____

➤ ➤ ➤ Our mothering friends need to offer us both grace and truth just as God himself does. They need to accept who we are and, at the same time, confront us with where we need to change. Who among your friends and support group plays that role in your life?

_____

_____

➤ ➤ ➤ Where will you go to find mothering friends if your list of those who offer you grace and truth is short or nonexistent?

_____

_____

OUR RESPONSE TO MOTHERING

Page 145

Having healthy and supportive friends is pointless if we don't receive what they offer. Cliff's story had a happy ending because he responded well to his support people. However, some adult children of Trophy Moms have good mothering available to them, yet they continue to thwart it.

➤➤➤ What is keeping you from taking the risk and opening up to the good mothering your friends are offering you?

_____

_____

_____

_____

➤➤➤ What will you do to overcome those barriers?

_____

_____

_____

_____

OUR PART IN OVERCOMING BEING A TROPHY

Page 146

➤➤➤ *Join.* Trophy deaths do not occur in a vacuum. You need to find an individual or a group where the traits of good-enough mothering are present.

❖ What group have you joined or what individual have you found that offers good enough mothering?

_____

_____

_____

❖ If you're still in a vacuum, what group will you join or what step will you take—this week—to find a source of good-enough mothering?

_____

_____

_____

➤ ➤ ➤ *Confess.* We need to agree with the reality and the truth of who we really are, acknowledging where we are lacking, so that we can receive acceptance, forgiveness, and love from God and from other people.

❖ What have you confessed and/or do you need to confess about where you are lacking?

_____

_____

_____

❖ Be specific about the "whatever is lacking" in you.

_____

_____

_____

➤ ➤ ➤ *Process negative feelings and losses.* An "ideal" person is not supposed to feel guilt, shame, failure, and pain, but one must process those feelings to bring the real self and the ideal self together.

❖ What are you doing or could you be doing to get in touch with the pain of your lost real self?

_____

_____

_____

❖ Complete the following statements:

I feel sad about letting go of the ideal and its _____

I'm hurting from _____

I'm angry that the trophy role demanded me to _____

➤ ➤ ➤ *Rework the ideal.* Adult children of Trophy Moms have a picture of their ideal self that is not even human.

❖ What parts of your ideal self are not humanly possible? What feelings, for instance, is your ideal self forbidden to feel?

_____

_____

❖   What facts about the normal human condition (such as struggle with temp-
    tation, sinfulness, and vulnerability) will you use to rework the ideal?

    _____

    _____

    _____

➤ ➤ ➤   *Learn to love less than the ideal.* Adult children of Trophy Moms can have a deep
disdain for imperfection in others, which they learned from their mother.

❖   What do you do, say, and/or think in response to other people's imperfec-
    tions? How much disdain, if any, do you feel toward others' imperfections?

    _____

    _____

    _____

❖   How can understanding the source of the contempt you feel help you move
    beyond that disdain to genuine acceptance of people as they are?

    _____

    _____

    _____

➤ ➤ ➤   *Challenge distorted thinking.* If you had a Trophy Mom, you may have distortions
in your thinking.

❖   What general distortions such as negative thought patterns, critical evalua-
    tion of yourself and others, and pessimism in your outlook on the future are
    you aware of? Start keeping track of how you think. Note automatic thought
    patterns and take the time to respond to them with true and positive words.

    _____

    _____

    _____

➤ ➤ ➤   *Accept failure.* To overcome the demands of the Trophy Mom and change your
attitude toward failure, you must begin to see failure as a normal part of the
human experience.

❖ Start noticing when you are making excuses, blaming others, or denying the emotions that come with failure.

_____

_____

_____

❖ What truth will you tell yourself about failure when you notice yourself making excuses, blaming others, or denying the emotions that come with failing?

_____

_____

_____

➤ ➤ ➤ *Monitor the emotional relationship between the real and the ideal.* We take our Trophy Mom's anger and condemnation into our real self, and it becomes the way we feel about our real self.

❖ What is the emotional tone of your attitude toward your real self—shaming, angry, condemning, attacking?

_____

_____

_____

❖ With what positive messages from your mothering people can you replace that negative attitude? God's attitudes toward you are a good model (p. 149).

_____

_____

_____

➤ ➤ ➤ *Repent.* A big part of ridding ourselves of the ideal demand is to take ownership of our real badness.

❖ Whom in your life do you trust to give you negative feedback?

_____

_____

_____

❖ What do you want to do, feel, say, and think when you are confronted with one of your faults? Develop a plan of healthy action.

_____

_____

_____

➤ ➤ ➤ *Pray.* The search for the real self is ultimately a spiritual one. But Trophy Moms teach their children to think and demand for themselves much more than God does and more than reality dictates.

❖ Which of mom's expectations and demands exceeded even God's demands? Be specific.

_____

_____

_____

❖ What role does or might God play in your discovery of your true self and your ability, courage, and strength to live out of your real self?

_____

_____

_____

➤ ➤ ➤ *Respond to love.* We need to take in the love that God and others offer us.

❖ How often do you respond to love with "You're just saying that" or "If you really knew me" reactions? Monitor your thoughts and feelings so that you can stop devaluing the love and good mothering others offer.

_____

_____

_____

❖ What will you do to let the love you receive penetrate?

_____

_____

_____

➤ ➤ ➤ *Watch for fears and resistance.* As you are loved and try to respond, you will feel fear and resistance.

❖ The real self has been alone and despised for a long time. What is it doing to fight your efforts to take it out of hiding?

_____

_____

_____

❖ What will you do to embrace your fear and resistance of grace and acceptance? What role will you let God play?

_____

_____

_____

DEALING WITH YOUR REAL MOM OF YESTERDAY

Page 150 After having responded to some good mothering from those in your community of support, you have to look at the real mom of the past. The process of dealing with the Trophy Mom involves awareness, feelings, forgiveness, and reconciliation. (See pp.82–83 for a description of the need for forgiveness.)

➤ ➤ ➤ *Be aware.*

❖ What kinds of interactions did you have with your mother that caused you to feel like a trophy? Be specific.

_____

_____

_____

❖ Who can give or has given you insight into these patterns?

_____

_____

_____

❖ What did you learn from how the man who, new to a professional setting, effectively identified and handled the voices in his head (p. 151)?

_____

_____

_____

➤ ➤ ➤ *Process the hurt feelings.*

❖ Begin by acknowledging the pain that came because your real self was rejected. Be specific. Put words to your grief over your wish for mom to accept you as you really are.

_____

_____

_____

❖ To whom will you express your anger and sadness? Grief brought into the light is the road to resolution and healing for your brokenheartedness.

_____

_____

_____

➤ ➤ ➤ *Understand her.*

❖ What of your mom's history—what she was struggling with, what kinds of demands were on her—can help you understand her and why she parented as she did?

_____

_____

_____

❖ Which of your mom's human frailties can you remind yourself of as you work on accepting her?

_____

_____

_____

➤ ➤ ➤ *Forgive.*

❖ Explain the paradox involved in forgiving the Trophy Mom (p. 152).

_____

_____

_____

❖ Evaluate where you are in your forgiveness process. Staying in touch with the hurt is normal, but are you still wanting to punish her or make her pay? What is the next step you need to take toward forgiving mom and freeing yourself from the past?

_____

_____

_____

If you are letting go of past hurts that you feel in relationship to mom and surrounding yourself with strong mothering in the present, you are ready to begin dealing with mom today.

YOUR RELATIONSHIP WITH MOM TODAY

Page 153 Parents, children, and grandchildren are created for relationship with one another. But how good can a relationship with a Trophy Mom get? What can you hope for?

➤ ➤ ➤ *Stop wanting acceptance.*

❖ Your mom's failure to accept the real you has everything to do with her. So remind yourself by summarizing here which of mom's issues and what aspects of her history kept her and may still keep her from accepting you as you are.

_____

_____

_____

_____

_____

❖ Your Trophy Mom has power over you in the present to the degree to which you still need her acceptance. To what degree do you need her acceptance? Who is offering you the acceptance you need?

_____

_____

_____

➤ ➤ ➤ *Talk it out.*

❖ Is talking out the Trophy Mom issue a possibility for you? How do you think your mom would respond?

_____

_____

_____

❖ If talking seems like an option, write out some rough ideas for what you might say to mom—your feelings, your fears, the pressure you feel to be "ideal," the dynamics that hinder your relationship with her. Be sure to reaffirm your love for her and thank her for listening.

_____

_____

_____

❖ When will you act? What will you ask your support group to do to help you take this step?

_____

_____

_____

MOTHERS WHO WON'T DEAL WITH THE ISSUE

Page 154 What can you hope for when mom won't deal with the issue?

➤ ➤ ➤ *Set limits.* How fragile you are feeling and how your mom is relating at the moment determine how much contact is too much.

❖ How fragile are you feeling these days? How would you handle a typical encounter with your Trophy Mom? What limits are wise for you right now?

_____

_____

_____

_____

❖ How is mom acting these days? Is she being especially hurtful? Or can you
shrug off the level of hurt with "That's just Mom"? What limits are wise for
you right now?

_____

_____

_____

➤ ➤ ➤ *Relate to her where she can.* Keep your interactions with your Trophy Mom in
safe areas.

❖ What areas of conversation and activities are safe? (It may be easier to answer that question by first listing topics and activities that are not safe.)

_____

_____

_____

❖ Have a plan for what you will do if mom gets off into performance despite
the presumably safe topic. What will you say?

_____

_____

_____

➤ ➤ ➤ *Love her where you can.*

❖ What kind of love is your Trophy Mom demanding? Remember that you can
choose how to love her.

_____

_____

_____

❖   In what ways are you able to love her? Be specific.

_____

_____

_____

CONCLUSION

Page 156   If you had a Trophy Mom, your task is to overcome the demand to be per-
            fect or ideal, to stop hiding from your imperfect parts.

➤ ➤ ➤   What summary statement is most encouraging? Which one is most challenging?

_____

_____

_____

_____

➤ ➤ ➤   What is the first action you will take as a result of working through these two
        chapters on the Trophy Mom? When will you take it? And from whom will you
        gain the support you need?

_____

_____

_____

_____

If you want to be healed, you must take your patterns of relating to a Trophy
Mom into relationship with God and other people.

*God, I have a lot of work to do to try to move on from the effects of having a
Trophy Mom. I also have a lot of work to do when it comes to relating with her
today. Help me grieve, forgive, and let go of the past and then help me to create
the best kind of relationship possible with her today. Amen.*

TEN ∾

The Still-the-Boss Mom

Sharon had definite principles, opinions, and values fixed in her mind. She had a worldview about lots of subjects: school, friendship, career, sexuality, finances, authority, and more—and her son Brad was her primary student in the "Sharon School of Thinking." As long as Brad agreed with Sharon's values, things went well, but Brad learned early on to go to others with his "taboo" questions. Sharon was a well-intentioned mother, but every approach she made to Brad carried one message: "No matter how old you get, I'll always be your mother." And, in fact, as Brad got older, mom was still the boss.

➤ ➤ ➤ What scenes—if any—from your own childhood does the story of Sharon and Brad's relationship (pp. 157–59) call to mind? Be specific about your mom's freely-voiced principles, opinions, and values. How is she still the boss today?

_____

_____

_____

_____

PREPARING FOR EQUALITY

Page 159 A good mother does more than nurture her child. She also constantly sees the potential adult in this child and behaves in a manner that elicits the grown-up from out of the kid. She wants to help develop a peer and a friend, not a grown child. The Controlling Mom injures the essence of the personality of the child while the Still-the-Boss Mom injures the child's ability to become an autonomous, functioning adult.

➤ ➤ ➤   *Authority.* Children start out with little authority and responsibility and must learn to gradually take on more. Mom needs to help them as they move into their place in the world of authority.

❖   Challenge. Mom needs to encourage her child to question her decisions and values. Doing so helps him come to a place of knowing what his own values are. How did your mom respond when you questioned her decisions and values? What did her response teach you?

_____

_____

_____

_____

❖   Are you able to challenge the thinking of your authority figures today? If so, give an example. If not, consider what you need to do to develop that ability.

_____

_____

_____

_____

❖   When have you needed to rebel appropriately against improper authorities? Be specific about the circumstances and the reasons why rebellion was appropriate. Did you rebel or not? Explain what you did or didn't do and why.

_____

_____

_____

_____

❖   Submission. We are to move beyond the stage of perpetual challenge and protest to an acceptance of our place in the world of authority. What did your mom model about submitting to authority?

_____

_____

_____

_____

❖ Describe the manner in which your mom asserted her authority within the home. Note the change you noticed (if any) as you grew up and assumed more responsibility in the home.

_____

_____

_____

_____

❖ Learning to both question and accept authority enables us to avoid the two destructive extremes of the fearfully compliant people-pleaser and the rebellious protester. Where are you on that spectrum?

_____

_____

_____

_____

➤ ➤ ➤ *Values*. Children need to learn good from bad and right from wrong. Teaching core values is a major parental responsibility.

❖ What values were clearly and effectively taught in your home? List several of the most important or most emphasized.

_____

_____

_____

_____

❖ What did mom do to help you learn to think for yourself? Share any specifics you remember and, based on how easy it is for you to think for yourself today, comment on how effective her teaching was.

_____

_____

_____

_____

❖ What did mom do to help you learn to think critically, to help you develop your "why" muscle? Again, share any specifics you remember and comment on how effective mom's teaching was.

_____

_____

_____

❖ What did mom teach, train, and model from her relationship with God? How has her teaching and modeling influenced your relationship with God?

_____

_____

_____

➤ ➤ ➤ *Talents.* To prepare for the adult world, children need to both become aware of and develop their unique gifts, talents, and abilities.

❖ When you think about the opportunities mom gave you to develop talents, would you say you were pursuing your interests or hers in order to please her? Explain.

_____

_____

_____

❖ Moms walk a fine line between allowing a child to develop his or her real, inborn talents through encouragement and guidance and forcing a child to develop those talents through pressure and discipline. How well did mom walk that line for you? Where did she push too much or not enough? What fruit has her encouragement or lack of it borne in your adult life?

_____

_____

_____

➤ ➤ ➤ *Gender Roles.* Preadolescent children are developing their sex roles, and mom is important.

❖ Review the discussion on page 164 of the text. Based on how comfortable you are with your sexuality today, describe how well mom helped you, her daughter, come to identify with her feminine qualities, or you, her son, identify with masculine roles and qualities.

_____

_____

_____

_____

❖ Who in your earlier years served as a positive same-sex model for you? What did that person teach you that you didn't learn at home?

_____

_____

_____

_____

➤ ➤ ➤ *Friendships.* In order to enter the adult world, children must learn to connect to people other than mom. They need to know how to relate to both sexes, people of different ages, and different types of individuals.

❖ What do you remember mom doing to help you make friends when you were growing up?

_____

_____

_____

_____

❖ What did you learn about the value of friendship from watching mom and her friends?

_____

_____

_____

_____

➤ ➤ ➤ *Adolescence*. This transitional period between childhood and adulthood is tumultuous and confusing for teen and mom alike.

❖ When you think back on your adolescence, what about mom—her actions, words, attitudes—do you remember? How did she respond to your typical adolescent behaviors—your challenges, questioning, and pushing against the limits?

_____

_____

_____

_____

❖ Consider now some specifics. Did mom have "taboo" subjects? Which battles (grades, church attendance, etc.) did she choose to fight? On what issues (dress, music, and so forth) did she give you freedom? Did she let character take precedence over style? Give an example to support your answer. What greater responsibility and greater freedom did she gradually give you? Finally, in general, how did mom respond to differences between you?

_____

_____

_____

_____

RESULTS OF STILL-THE-BOSS MOTHERING

Page 167   Several signs indicate that the child of a Still-the-Boss Mom has had problems moving into the grownup years.

➤ ➤ ➤ *Relational Signs*. Which of these signs, if any, characterize your behavior, suggesting some difficulty relating to others as equal adults? (See descriptions on pp. 167–69.)

___ One-down style (persistently feel inferior to others)
___ One-up style (feeling one-down but adopting a superior role and aspiring to lead and control others)
___ Rebellious style

➤ ➤ ➤ *Functional Signs.* These "not-quite-adults" may also have problems related to goals, success, and general functioning.

❖ As a child of a Still-the-Boss Mom, are you afraid of disapproval, attempting to be parental, or hating all parents? Support your answer with specifics.

_____

_____

_____

❖ How easily do you set goals for yourself? Are you concerned about setting the "right " goals? Do you have a problem with follow-through? Do you fear success? Explain how the tendencies you identified may be connected to your Still-the-Boss Mom.

_____

_____

_____

➤ ➤ ➤ *Emotional Signs.* Which of these signs, if any, do you deal with?

___ Anxiety
___ Depression
___ Obsessive-compulsive disorder
___ Substance problem
___ Sexual addiction
___ Compulsive behavior
___ Impulsive behavior

➤ ➤ ➤ *Spiritual Signs.* Consider your experience with God.

❖ Do you view God as a harsh, dictatorial judge? If so, how has that view affected your relationship with him? What passages of the Bible tend to jump out at you? Comment on how wholeheartedly you believe God loves you.

_____

_____

_____

❖ Do you view God in intellectualized, black-and-white, or legalistic ways? If so, how has that view affected your approach to spiritual matters and your relationship with God? How do you deal with the mystery, paradoxes, and unknowable parts of God?

_____

_____

_____

_____

NOWADAYS WITH MOM

Page 171   As they grow up, "not-quite" adults have several problems relating to mom.

➤ ➤ ➤ Do you see yourself in any of these scenarios? If so, which ones?

    ____Regressing when you visit mom

    ____Attempting to make mom recognize that you are okay and gain her approval

    ____Having her approval—yet resenting having to answer to mom for everything

    ____Engaging in major conflicts

    ____Disengaging from each other

➤ ➤ ➤ What hurts or lessons learned growing up are behind the behaviors you noted above?

_____

_____

_____

_____

_____

The "permanent child" struggles in many areas, but the next chapter outlines a process to repair the undeveloped adult parts of the character.

God, I'm not very good at being an adult—but now I see some reasons why. And this authority issue is tricky for me—but I'm understanding a little bit more what's behind my struggle. I also see more clearly why I don't relate very well to you or to other people. But I'm ready to try to stop being a "permanent child" and become an adult. Please help me. Amen.

ELEVEN ❧

Rebuilding Your Adulthood

Distinguishing between the Controlling Mom and the Still-the-Boss Mom can be confusing because at times these two can sound like the same issue. In a sense they are, but with a little different emphasis.

➤ ➤ ➤ Review the discussion on page 173 and then explain in your own words the difference between the Controlling Mom and the Still-the-Boss Mom. Was yours a Controlling Mom or a Still-the-Boss Mom? Support your answer with feelings you have about functioning in an adult's world.

_____

_____

_____

_____

➤ ➤ ➤ What thoughts and feelings do you have when you consider becoming an equal with your adult mother?

_____

_____

_____

_____

THE NEW PEER GROUP

Page 173   The concept of having to grow up after you are grown up may be strange to you, but it may be a task you need to tackle.

➤ ➤ ➤ If you're thinking, "But I haven't lived with my mother for years. How can I still be a child?" you may be able to answer this question by answering the following questions.

❖ How do you feel when you disagree with other adults?

_____

_____

❖ How do you feel when you have an opinion different from an authority figure? Can you express that opinion?

_____

_____

❖ Are you judgmental of others?

_____

_____

❖ Do you feel inferior or superior to others instead of equal?

_____

_____

❖ Do you feel confident in your own decisions?

_____

_____

❖ Do you feel comfortable with your sexuality?

_____

_____

❖ Do you recognize and pursue your talents?

_____

_____

❖ Can you submit to people in authority without conflict?

_____

_____

❖ Can you value and love people who are different?

_____

_____

➤ ➤ ➤ Summarize what you've seen about yourself in your answers to the preceding questions. In what areas do you need to work on moving toward adulthood?

_____

_____

_____

_____

➤ ➤ ➤ Remember Samantha and the preschool decision she faced? When she received contradictory advice from two people who were always right, she didn't know whom to listen to or what decision to make. When have you encountered a similar dilemma? What did you do? How did you handle the decision-making process? What feelings resulted?

_____

_____

_____

_____

You would like to be able to listen to the advice of wise people, weigh it for yourself, and make your own decision. But how do you get there if you have had a Still-the-Boss Mom and always turn other people into parents? Let's look and see.

STEP ONE: GET SICK AND TIRED ENOUGH TO MAKE A CHANGE

Page 175   The truth is that you don't have to let other adults parent you.

➤ ➤ ➤ In the last year, which adults have parented you?

_____

_____

_____

➤ ➤ ➤ How do you feel about living under the demands and expectations of all the "mothers" of the world, feeling judged every time you don't do what they think you should?

_____

_____

_____

_____

➤ ➤ ➤ Are you sick and tired enough to do something about having all these parents in your life? Do you want to be your own adult? How will you use your anger and tiredness to fuel the revolution against the Still-the-Boss Mom inside and establish your own government?

_____

_____

_____

_____

STEP TWO: FIND YOUR TRUE PEER GROUP

`Page 176`   To become an equal with mother, you must join the adult world as a peer.

➤ ➤ ➤ Whom in your life do you treat as parents because they treat you as a child?

_____

_____

➤ ➤ ➤ Who in your life supports your attempts to become equal with them? Who respects your freedom and ability to think for yourself, ask questions, have your own opinions, and take risks?

_____

_____

_____

_____

➤ ➤ ➤ What would it mean to you to be your own person? What specific new thought patterns, freedoms, activities, and choices would you enjoy?

_____

_____

_____

_____

_____

THE NEW TASKS WITH OTHER ADULTS

`Page 176` You left some tasks undone in your growing-up years. Let's look at what you must do to complete them now.

➤ ➤ ➤ 1. Reevaluate beliefs. To be a true adult, you need to work out your own beliefs and values rather than inheriting without question your beliefs from your parents.

❖ What do *you* think about . . .

Church _____

_____

Religion _____

_____

Politics _____

_____

Finances _____

_____

Childrearing _____

_____

Minorities _____

_____

Your career _____

_____

❖ How can your support people help you work out your own beliefs and values? (Make sure your beliefs and values are yours even if they turn out to be the same as mom's.)

_____

_____

_____

_____

➤ ➤ ➤ 2. Disagree with authority figures. If you had a Still-the-Boss Mom, you may have to push yourself to voice your opinions when you're around authority figures.

❖ Remember Roger? When have you had important information but were afraid to speak up? What kept you from sharing what you knew or thought?

_____

_____

_____

_____

❖ When have you overcome that fear? If you can't think of a recent example, consider how your support group can help you learn to disagree with authority figures.

_____

_____

_____

_____

➤ ➤ ➤ 3. Make your own decisions. Those stuck in the Still-the-Boss Mom syndrome fear displeasing their mother figures and are always deferring to what the mother figures think.

❖ In what areas of life do you especially struggle with decision making?

_____

_____

_____

❖ What decision are you facing now? What option would please mom? What option do you prefer but hesitate to act on? What knowledgeable person will you go to for advice? How will you handle the possible later realization that you didn't make a wise decision? How will your support group help at that point?

_____

_____

_____

_____

_____

_____

_____

_____

_____

➤ ➤ ➤ 4. Deal with your sexuality. Children are repressed sexually; adults are not. If you are still in the child position with mom, then you are probably suffering sexual consequences of some type.

❖ What are *your* (not mom's) values, feelings, thoughts, and opinions about sex?

_____

_____

_____

_____

❖ With whom will you talk about your sexuality? How might you benefit from talking about your sexuality with your peers?

_____

_____

_____

_____

➤ ➤ ➤ 5. Give yourself permission to be equal with your parents. Sounds simple, but many people feel guilty for assuming an adult position with their Still-the-Boss Mom.

❖ Is it okay to be equal with mom? Why or why not?

_____

_____

_____

_____

❖ Does it feel bad to have just as many rights and privileges as mom does? Do you still feel that you must obey all of mom's wishes? Explain your answers.

_____

_____

_____

_____

➤ ➤ ➤ 6. Recognize and pursue your talents and dreams. Children dream of what they will one day do. Adults go and study, practice, risk, and build—they do it!

❖ What negative thinking is keeping you from trying to discover what you are good at and going for it?

_____

_____

_____

_____

❖ What will you do to take responsibility for your gifts and talents?

_____

_____

_____

_____

➤ ➤ ➤ 7. Practice. Many people still under mom's authority as adults are so afraid of failure—of not doing something right the first time—that they don't practice.

❖ Describe a time when you risked, failed, got feedback, and tried again. What
   did you learn? Did you experience joy or did an internal, critical mom's judgment interfere?

_____

_____

_____

_____

❖ What current situation in your life provides you an opportunity to practice
   acting like an adult and to take a step toward adulthood?

_____

_____

_____

_____

➤ ➤ ➤ 8. Gain authority over acting out. When we feel as though we are under the par-
        ent, we rebel against rules, even the ones we set for ourselves.

❖ What rule(s) are hardest for you to obey?

_____

_____

_____

_____

❖ The way out of impulse problems caused by adolescent rebellion in adults is
   not to try harder but to get out of the one-down position to the parent. What
   will you do to get out of the one-down position? How can your support system and some accountability help you?

_____

_____

_____

_____

➤ ➤ ➤   9. Submit out of freedom. True adults can submit to authority structures without a fight.

❖   When has it been hard for you to submit to an authority? Be specific regarding the circumstances and especially the feelings you had about yourself as you considered submitting.

_____

_____

_____

_____

❖   Summarize an adult's attitude toward submission and why it isn't an admission that you are less of a person than the authority to whom you are submitting.

_____

_____

_____

_____

➤ ➤ ➤   10. Do good works. A hallmark of true adult identity is using your gifts and talents to give back to the world.

❖   What can you give back to the world through your gifts and talents? Be specific.

_____

_____

_____

_____

❖   Why will or does giving back to the world signify freedom from a Still-the-Boss Mom?

_____

_____

_____

_____

➤ ➤ ➤ 11. Love people who are different. Learning to appreciate people who are different and love them for who they are is a key step toward adult maturity.

❖ Whom in your life—or even in the world at large—do you find difficult to accept, much less love?

_____

_____

_____

_____

❖ What will you do to identify and discard the prejudices that keep you from accepting and loving these people?

_____

_____

_____

_____

As long as you continue in an immature behavior, you will perpetuate the immature child in your life and will not reach the maturity you desire. An accountability support system can help you take these important but difficult steps toward getting out from under the Still-the-Boss Mom and on the road to adulthood.

DEALING WITH MOTHER OF THE PAST

Page 180

By now you have seen the pattern of dealing with the past mom of various types in your head. The process of dealing with the Still-the-Boss Mom is the same.

➤ ➤ ➤ Find a safe place with people who support your growing up and becoming an adult.

❖ Where is that safe place for you—or where do you think you might find it?

_____

_____

_____

_____

➤ ➤ ➤   Gain awareness of the relational patterns you got from your Still-the-Boss Mom.

❖   What have this chapter and the last revealed to you about which Still-the-Boss Mom patterns are yours? What relational patterns do you need to change? Summarize what you've learned about yourself.

_____

_____

_____

_____

_____

➤ ➤ ➤   Process the feelings involved—resentment, sadness, anger, grief, or whatever you are carrying around.

❖   What feelings are you carrying around? Identify them now and then feel them.

_____

_____

_____

_____

Doing so is key to getting rid of them and keeping them from hindering your relationship with mom and others.

➤ ➤ ➤   Challenge the Still-the-Boss Mom messages that you have internalized and that speak now as your own critical or limiting voice inside.

❖   What messages inside your head encourage you to remain a child? Keep a record of them and then challenge those automatic beliefs with truthful messages and the "you can" voices of your support people.

_____

_____

_____

_____

➤ ➤ ➤ Forgive. Let mom off the hook and then both of you can be free of the past that haunts you and keeps you down.

❖ Turn back to chapter 5 and the discussion of forgiveness (pp. 82–83). Where are you in the process? What is the next step you need to take toward forgiving mom?

_____

_____

_____

_____

DEALING WITH RESISTANCE

Page 182 It's strange how we resist the very thing we need and have been longing for.

➤ ➤ ➤ What tendencies to resist adulthood and freedom, to escape equality, and to return to the child position with your mother figures are you aware of? Review the list below—and ask your support people to do the same so that they can watch for these behaviors and call you on them.

___ Blaming your inactivity on others
___ Excusing your lack of performance on external factors
___ Complaining about your mother as if she is the one keeping you from doing what you want to be doing
___ Griping about authority figures as if they have control of you
___ Getting down on yourself for failure and resist the practice cycle
___ Whining about your lack of talents and abilities instead of pursuing them
___ Bowing down to figures you have placed on pedestals
___ Repressing your own opinions
___ Seeking approval or trying to avoid disapproval from equal adults
___ Settling into a "taking" position to avoid service
___ Dreaming instead of "doing"

➤ ➤ ➤ How do you want to respond when your support/accountability partners confront you about your unhealthy, immature behaviors? Develop a specific response that reminds you that they are giving you feedback that you asked for as an adult.

_____

_____

_____

NEW RELATIONSHIP WITH MOM

Page 183 Whether or not your Still-the-Boss Mom recognizes it, you are the one in control of your own life now. She may, however, not know quite what to do with the new you.

➤ ➤ ➤ *The Ideal.* Ideally, you and your Still-the-Boss Mom would talk out your problems and work through them. The goal is to preserve your adulthood and to preserve the friendship with your mom.

❖ Plan what you would like to say to her and how you will explain what you as an adult want in your relationship with her. Review the guidelines discussed on pages 183–85. Be specific about how you will address each of the following items.

◆ What can you affirm about her and the parenting job she did?

_____

_____

◆ What words and points will you avoid to keep from sounding like a victim?

_____

_____

◆ What will you say about wanting to be friends and needing her respect?

_____

_____

◆ How will you ask her to confront you when she sees you reverting back to being a child with her?

_____

_____

◆ What do you expect from mom in the way of calls, visits, advice, and ways of relating?

_____

_____

◆ Are you ready to apologize and ask forgiveness for ways she says you have hurt her? What have you said or done in anger that you need to ask forgiveness for?

_____

_____

◆ What ideas for new things that two of you can do as friends will you suggest?

_____

_____

❖ As you get ready to talk to mom, try to anticipate her various reactions so that you will be prepared to deal with whatever happens. How will you let your support people be there for you before and after you talk to mom?

_____

_____

_____

_____

➤ ➤ ➤ *Not-So-Good Situations.* If mom cannot respect you as an equal adult and wants to continue to dominate and rule you to varying degrees, you have to take a different route. Here the goal is to preserve your adulthood and act responsibly toward mom.

❖ First, why is it important for your own growth that you act responsibly toward mom?

_____

_____

_____

_____

❖ Following each of the following ten tips, remind yourself why each is important and, after reviewing the description of each (pp. 185–88), develop a specific action step for each. How will you live out each in your particular situation?

◆ 1. Grieve your wish that mom see you and treat you as an adult.

_____

_____

◆ 2. Do not respond in anger.

_____

_____

◆ 3. Do not respond out of guilt.

_____

_____

◆ 4. Feel free to disagree.

_____

_____

◆ 5. Set limits on yourself.

_____

_____

◆ 6. Set limits with mom.

_____

_____

◆ 7. Use your support system.

_____

_____

◆ 8. Relate to mom's strengths.

_____

_____

◆ 9. Above all, love your mom.

_____

_____

It really is possible to honor your Still-the-Boss Mom as mom, love her as you do yourself, and be in charge of your own life.

Well, God, I've caught a glimpse of what full adulthood means. The eleven steps toward that adulthood aren't easy, but the freedom that awaits seems worth the risk and the effort. And there certainly is risk and effort involved in talking to mom about the growth I'm experiencing and/or want to experience. Please be with me as I work on improving my relationship with mom—and as I learn to be an adult. Amen.

TWELVE ~

The American Express Mom

Leaving home was a process full of conflict for Catherine. Her mother, Joyce, had prided herself on the independence and feistiness of her firstborn daughter, but conflicts arose when Catherine made choices that took her outside the actual definition of the family. Joyce often won by playing on Catherine's guilt. Whether the decision involved which youth group to attend, which college to go to, or what to do during Christmas vacation, Catherine felt like a child who still had to obey her parents at every turn.

➤ ➤ ➤ What scenes from your own growing-up years does the story of Joyce and Catherine's relationship (pp. 189–91) bring to mind? Be specific about points of conflict, times you gave in to mom's pressure, and the feelings that accompanied both the discussion and the ensuing action.

_____

_____

_____

_____

GUARDIANS AND MANAGERS

Page 191
"Leaving home" is all about taking over the governmental aspects of one's life. A good guardian and manager (mom) will gradually delegate this freedom.

134

➤ ➤ ➤ What gradual delegation of freedom, if any, do you remember mom extending you as you grew up?

_____

_____

_____

_____

➤ ➤ ➤ Today you may live thousands of miles away from mom and you may be a parent yourself. But are you still under mom's guardianship and management? In what way?

_____

_____

_____

_____

This chapter deals with being separate and independent while still "under" mom and then moving out from that role into adulthood. Let's see what this process looks like and what is involved in making it happen.

ADOLESCENCE: THE BEGINNING OF LEAVING

`Page 191` We looked at some developmental aspects of adolescence in chapter 11. In this chapter, we'll see the aspects of adolescence that specifically affect the child's ability to leave mother when the time comes. Listed below are some important aspects of adolescence that prepare someone to leave home.

➤ ➤ ➤ *Experience of the larger world.* Discovery of the outside world lets adolescents know the world has more to offer than what their parents have shown them and teaches them that they can negotiate the world without holding a parent's hand.

❖ Which of the following elements of adolescence came relatively easily to you? Comment on how they prepared you to leave home.

___ Getting a driver's license _____

___ Extracurricular activities _____

___ Concerts _____

____ Sports _____
____ Service clubs _____
____ Trips with friends _____
____ Hobbies_____
____ Dating _____

❖ Go through the list again, this time noting mom's response to your activities.

____ Getting a driver's license _____
____ Extracurricular activities _____
____ Concerts _____
____ Sports _____
____ Service clubs _____
____ Trips with friends _____
____ Hobbies_____
____ Dating _____

➤ ➤ ➤ *Increasing power of the peer group.* The later adolescent becomes increasingly dependent on her peer group for emotional and social support. The peer group also becomes a powerful influence of values and norms. Her sense of where she belongs is slowly enlarged to include not just her family but also her peers.

❖ Think back to your late adolescent years. Describe the role your peer group played in your life. What kind of emotional and social support did they offer? What values did they influence? What norms did they provide?

_____
_____
_____
_____

❖ What do you remember about mom's reactions to or comments about your friends, classmates, and peer group?

_____
_____
_____
_____

➤ ➤ ➤ *Increasing experience of the limits of the outside world.* If mom can stay out of the way of the outside world's limits, the child learns that parents are not the only ones with rules.

❖ Describe an experience or two you had as an adolescent (trouble at school, on the job, or with the law, for instance) that helped you see that parents aren't the only ones with rules.

_____

_____

_____

_____

❖ What do you remember about mom's reactions to your experiences of the outside world's limits?

_____

_____

_____

_____

➤ ➤ ➤ *Toward financial independence.* The more the teen enters the world, the more money is required. Mother's role is to allow and encourage the teen's separateness and independence while at the same time setting limits on her child's regressive wish to be taken care of.

❖ What did you do to earn money during your adolescent years?

_____

_____

_____

_____

❖ What kind of support did mom offer? Too much? Too little? Explain.

_____

_____

_____

_____

LATE ADOLESCENCE AND EARLY ADULTHOOD

Page 196 As the child moves through the years of adolescence and begins to look at
adulthood, the reality of leaving home unfolds. The parent gradually turns
over the management of the child to the child.

➤ ➤ ➤ Think back to your late adolescence. How did you feel about the prospect of leaving
home? What do you remember about your mother's attitude toward your leaving?

_____

_____

_____

_____

➤ ➤ ➤ To the extent that a person is being parented, the person is still a child.

❖ To what extent were you being parented when you were eighteen? Twenty-
five? To what extent are you being parented today?

_____

_____

_____

_____

❖ Somewhere to live, somewhere to work, her own friends and support network,
her own spiritual life, and paying for it all—these are indicators of leaving home.
In which areas have you left home? Where do you have some work to do?

_____

_____

_____

_____

➤ ➤ ➤ The Mother's Wound. The essential reality is that mom gets abandoned. The relationship is not over, but it is changing. Mother is no longer *the* source.

❖ What insight into a mother's experience did you gain from reading this section?

_____

_____

_____

_____

❖ What insight into your own mother's behavior and the mothering she gave you did you gain from this section?

_____

_____

_____

_____

RESULTS OF AMERICAN EXPRESS MOTHERING

Page 197   Certain signs and symptoms indicate if things are not going well in the separating process.

➤ ➤ ➤ *Relational Signs*

❖ Which of these signs characterize your behavior, suggesting unhealthy dependency that has its roots in an American Express Mom? (See descriptions on pp. 198–99.)

___ "Mother Me, Please—How Dare You Mother Me!" (likes the caretaking but resents the control)

___ Abandoning the partner (divorce, breakup, or avoiding emotional intimacy)

___ Avoidance of adult connections

___ Idealizing (remaining safely tied to mom and devaluing others)

___ Caretaking

➤ ➤ ➤ *Functional Signs*

❖ Which of these signs are evident in your life, especially in work and parenting roles? (See descriptions on pages 101–3.)

___ Disorganization

___ Developmental problems in the areas of identity and talent

___ Problems delaying gratification

___ Other signs of irresponsibility

➤ ➤ ➤ *Emotional Signs*

    ❖ Which of the following do you deal with? (See descriptions on pages 103–5.)

        ___ Depression

        ___ Feelings of powerlessness

        ___ Sense of helplessness

        ___ Addictions, with mother bailing you out of the consequences

        ___ Isolation

        ___ Anxiety

        ___ Panic attacks

        ___ Being a "blamer"

➤ ➤ ➤ *Spiritual Signs*

    ❖ Evaluate your relationship with God. What are you doing to take responsibility for it? Offer specific evidence. Is your relationship with God more like that of a grandchild than a child? Explain. How are you still answering more to mom than to God? Be specific.

_____

_____

_____

_____

True maturity is when we stop asking life to meet our demands and begin to meet the demands of life. A mother who is either the holder of the demands or the one who meets them for her adult child actually hinders the child's growth in maturity.

WHAT IT LOOKS LIKE NOW

Page 200   If you are still connected to your mother in an unhealthy way, you are avoiding the separation and independence of being an adult.

➤ ➤ ➤ If you've had an American Express Mom, you may have current problems in one of more of the following. Identify which one(s) and add details.

        ___ Finances

        ___ Daily functioning

___ Establishing a "home base" of your own

___ Building an emotional support system away from the family

___ Relating to in-laws

___ Breaking away from pleasing mother

___ Avoiding an adult relationship with mother

___ Argumentative relationship with mother

___ Codependent ties with mother

___ Tendency to live out mother's dreams for your life and career instead of pursuing your own

___ Struggles to achieve a mature sexual identity and functioning

_____

_____

_____

_____

➤ ➤ ➤ What are you doing, or what will you do, to take responsibility for the problems you just identified?

_____

_____

_____

_____

SIGN OF MATURITY NOW WITH MOM

Page 201   A good relationship with your mother is a sign of health, and it is rewarding for parents and grown children alike.

➤ ➤ ➤ Who in your life models a good relationship with one or both parents? What do you admire? What factors contribute to that good relationship?

_____

_____

_____

_____

_____

➤ ➤ ➤ What kind of relationship would you like to have with your mom? Be specific.

_____

_____

_____

_____

To truly enjoy mother in our adult years, we must emotionally leave home first. We must do the tasks we have been talking about, and in the next chapter, you'll learn how.

God, I've gained some insight into a mother's role and specifically into my mom's role. I now have some compassion to offset my real desire to "leave home." I'm overwhelmed by the work that leaving home will involve, but I'm ready to try. I'm ready to be on my own at last. Please help me. Amen.

THIRTEEN ∿

Leaving Home the Right Way

As we saw in chapter 12, we need to leave mother in real, practical, day-to-day ways. We are created to "abandon" her and set up our own home and support system.

➤ ➤ ➤ What about yourself, if anything, did you see in the Jo/Mark/Shannon story—the details, behaviors, and attitudes? Explain.

_____

_____

_____

_____

➤ ➤ ➤ At this point, in what real, practical, day-to-day ways do you need to leave your mother?

_____

_____

_____

_____

What follows is a structure for this last task: the decision to leave the child's role and come into your own as a grown-up in a grown-up's world.

THE LONGEST YARD

Page 204 The task of leaving mom in your everyday life is the longest yard of growth, as it involves making painful adjustments to long-standing patterns.

➤➤➤ If you are still going to mom for things you should be providing for yourself, you will always be a prisoner to your relationship with her—and that's not mom's fault.

❖ What things is mom providing that you as an adult should be providing for yourself? Be specific.

_____

_____

_____

❖ How do those things make you a prisoner? Again, be specific.

_____

_____

_____

_____

➤➤➤ Are you fighting her "control" like Mark? Are you trying not to upset her like Shannon? Describe your attitudes and actions when it comes to relating to mom.

_____

_____

_____

TASKS

Page 205 Let's look at several of the important tasks you can undertake to begin leaving mom in your everyday life and living deliberately, autonomously, and according to your own values and directions.

➤➤➤ *Develop your new "home" before you leave.* No matter how motivated, miserable, or mad you are at your situation with mom, don't even think about leaving your American Express connection until you have created, developed, and stabilized your own emotional home base.

❖ Why is this wise advice?

_____

_____

_____

_____

❖ Consider your closest friends. Can you share painful feelings, be dependent, and reveal your "bad self" to them? What does your answer tell you about the security of your current emotional home base?

_____

_____

_____

_____

❖ The best way to determine the status of your emotional home base is to ask these people you trust how intimate they think you are with them. Whom will you ask this week?

➤➤➤ *Answer to your support relationships.* Close relationships without responsibility are not enough. We need to take the counsel of our friends seriously.

❖ What truth about yourself has your friends' love enabled you to hear and accept? Be specific about that truth and how you might have responded to it had it come from a different source or in a different manner. Explain how your friends' presence helped you grow.

_____

_____

_____

_____

❖ Becoming answerable to your support relationships is key to creating your own home. In which of the following areas are you willing to hear your friends express their perspectives and opinions?

___ How you handle your relationships
___ How responsible you are
___ Your conduct and character
___ How you deal with your marriage
___ Your parenting style
___ Your physical condition and habits
___ Your spiritual life
___ Your finances
___ Your work habits and directions
___ How you maintain the house

❖ What does your answer show you about yourself and your willingness to answer to your support relationships? What, if anything, is keeping you from wanting to hear their perspectives and opinions?

_____

_____

_____

_____

❖ Again, consult your safe friends: "How am I doing on the leaving-home end of things? Do you see me having any problems in cutting the cord?" Listen to their realities.

_____

_____

_____

_____

➤ ➤ ➤ Next, begin to develop a sense of "no excuses ownership" over your successes and failures. Let that replace your American Express Mom's tendency to blame or rationalize.

❖ What does it mean to evaluate a failure or problem from a "character before circumstances" perspective (see p. 208)? What can a person who does this learn?

_____

_____

_____

_____

❖ Think back over the last month or so. What is one situation you can look at from a "character before circumstances" perspective? What do you learn when you start taking responsibility by asking how you contributed to that failure or problem?

_____

_____

_____

_____

➤ ➤ ➤ *Cherish your spouse.* Children of the American Express Mom often wreak havoc in their marriages.

❖ As a child of an American Express Mom, are you . . .

___ Comparing your spouse unfavorably to mom?
___ Wanting to overinvolve your spouse with her life?
___ Trying to get the spouse to take sides in some argument with mom?

❖ How is this action weakening your marriage?

_____

_____

_____

_____

❖ What steps will you take to begin cherishing your spouse?

_____

_____

_____

_____

❖ What will you do to involve your spouse in your efforts to "leave home"? What kind of help do you want your spouse to give you as you strive to cherish him/her over mom?

_____

_____

_____

_____

➤ ➤ ➤ *Bring mom in on the process.* Many moms aren't in denial about these issues; they simply were raised a certain way and didn't know any alternative ways to rear their children.

❖ How do you think your mom would respond if you told her that you are working on "leaving home" and becoming a grown-up in a grown-up's world and that you'd like her help?

_____

_____

_____

_____

❖ How will you respond if mom is hurt when you ask her to help you abandon her? Whom will you turn to for support?

_____

_____

_____

_____

➤ ➤ ➤ *Manage your money.* Finances are probably the single most measurable, quantifiable, and observable gauge of how you're doing in leaving your American Express Mom.

❖ What money symptom(s) do you exhibit?

___ Help during tax time
___ Luxury expenses
___ Emergencies

_____ Privileges the kids couldn't have otherwise
_____ Other:_____

❖ What steps will you take to take hold of your finances and learn to live within your means?

_____ Lower your standard of living
_____ Learn to budget and save
_____ Delay gratification
_____ Get budgeting help from a finance expert or a wise friend
_____ Other:_____

❖ If you're thinking about borrowing money from mom or already have, what will you do to treat her as a bank, with all the protection and benefits due the lender? Be specific.

_____

_____

_____

_____

➤ ➤ ➤ *Be responsible for functional tasks.* Too many people stay dependent on mom for things they should be doing for themselves.

❖ Which of the following is mom doing that you should be doing?

_____ Laundry
_____ Home furnishings
_____ Insurance policies
_____ Babysitting
_____ Affordable entertainment
_____ Running errands and picking the kids up at school
_____ Cleaning house
_____ Vacations
_____ Making decisions
_____ Other:_____

❖ When will you take the first step toward phasing mom out of doing these functional tasks?

_____

_____

_____

_____

➤ ➤ ➤ *Parent your kids.* Adults who haven't left home often want to be their own children's "best friend." They fear the authority and the distance the adult role necessarily brings with children.

❖ What do you struggle with that keeps you from authoritative parenting?

___ Being in charge
___ Confronting
___ Setting limits
___ Handling a child's rage
___ Other:_____

❖ What will you do to learn more about healthy parenting?

_____

_____

_____

_____

➤ ➤ ➤ *Take charge of your own self-development.* You can enjoy the benefits of being a responsible, grown, independent adult in three important dimensions.

❖ Talents: You are a craftsperson at something. Is it artistic, financial, spiritual, athletic, or professional? What are you doing or will you do to develop that special gift as well as other unique strengths and talents?

_____

_____

_____

_____

❖ Sexuality: In what ways, if any, is your sexuality underdeveloped? Do you need to grow into your gender role? Do you need to grow in tenderness and passion with your spouse? What will you do to foster that growth?

_____

_____

_____

_____

❖ Taking risks: Dream! Explore! Find challenges and opportunities. What would you like to do regarding a career change, travel, appropriate lifestyle changes, spiritual life, and/or cultural exploration? Be specific—and then act.

_____

_____

_____

_____

REVAMPING YOURSELF WITH MOM

Page 211 Leaving your American Express Mom means leaving the role and the dynamic, not the person. You can keep a good connection with mother, but it will change as you change. Here are the tasks you need to perform.

➤➤➤ *Establish a friendship.* Friendship is a mutual connection between two equal adults. This friendship with mom is not a survival relationship; rather, it's an enjoyment of one another's company.

❖ In what specific ways, if any, are you still dependent on mom for survival? Which one will you let go of first?

_____

_____

_____

_____

❖ What mutually enjoyed activities could you do together? Which one would
   be a good one to start with?

_____

_____

_____

_____

➤ ➤ ➤ *Receive favors, not needs.* Gratefully receive the favors, but set limits with yourself and mom here.

❖ Are mom's gifts to you—of cash, products, or services—extras or essentials?
   Be honest with yourself.

_____

_____

_____

_____

❖ What will you say to explain to mom that you appreciate her generosity but
   can't be receiving from her things you need, plan for, depend on, or budget
   for?

_____

_____

_____

_____

➤ ➤ ➤ *Decide how to help.* It is your responsibility to give back to her for what she has
given.

❖ How can you make a return to mom?

_____

_____

_____

_____

❖ Ask yourself the following questions and discuss them with your support people. Note your initial thoughts here.

◆ Is mom's need small or severe?

_____

_____

_____

◆ What resources does she have to provide for her own needs (friends, church, finances, and so forth)?

_____

_____

_____

◆ What is your level of responsibility? How much of a relationship was there and is there?

_____

_____

_____

◆ What are your own resources and responsibilities? Will helping mom compromise your family's needs or can you provide adequately for both?

_____

_____

_____

❖ Review the notes you just made. What kind of emotional and functional support does mom need now? What is the extent of your return to her right now?

_____

_____

_____

_____

➤ ➤ ➤ *Decide if or how you will parent mom.* Although the American Express Mom may have social relationships, her dependencies often lie with her children. She may see her kids as her emotional retirement fund.

❖ Do you feel as if you're the parent and mom's the child? Explain. Support your answer with specific evidence. What is mom demanding in the way of relationship, support, and time?

_____

_____

_____

_____

_____

❖ Spend a few minutes thinking about what you can give emotionally as a friend to your mother. Think about your available time and your responsibilities to self, God, family, work, and friends. What can you do to help mom find friendships? What will you say to explain to mom that you will wholeheartedly spend time with her, but that there's only so much of you to go around?

_____

_____

_____

_____

➤ ➤ ➤ *Learn from your anger.* Anger signals a problem. We need to first figure out what our anger is about and then use it in our relationship with mom.

❖ Are you experiencing intrusion anger and/or wish disappointment? (See definitions on p. 215 of the text.) Use your supportive remothering relationships to help you separate the two. Explain what is behind each.

_____

_____

_____

_____

❖ What will you say when you confront mom about the issues behind your intrusion anger? When will you begin processing your wish disappointment with your support group?

_____

_____

_____

_____

➤ ➤ ➤ *The mother-in-law.* Mother problems are often mother-in-law problems. Problems arise if your spouse still hasn't left his or her own American Express Mom.

❖ Has your spouse left his or her American Express Mom? If not, support your answer with a few specifics about arguments you get pulled into or times your spouse and mom have ganged up on you.

_____

_____

_____

_____

❖ What will you say to help your spouse see that he or she isn't functioning as a spouse with you? See some possible conversation starters on page 216.

_____

_____

_____

_____

❖ What will you do to work out your own relationship with your mother-in-law? How, for instance, will you avoid triangulations?

_____

_____

_____

_____

WHAT IT CAN BE LIKE

Page 216 What can happen as you leave the American Express mom relationship and begin to shoulder your own adult load?

➤ ➤ ➤ Mom may not respond well.

❖ Where will you find support if your experience is a lot like Megan's?

_____

_____

_____

_____

❖ What do you respect about how Megan dealt with her American Express Mom?

_____

_____

_____

_____

➤ ➤ ➤ Mom may understand the issue.

❖ What did you learn from the way Brendan dealt with his American Express Mom?

_____

_____

_____

_____

❖ What will you say when you explain that you want a friendship with mom? What necessary changes will you identify? What will you do to help her find new friends?

_____

_____

_____

_____

We've worked through the six mothering types and the attendant problems and solutions. We hope that, if you've seen yourself, you are now able to follow the tasks involved in developing what you didn't get the first time around. In the next section, we will look at the special problems that women and then men face in their mother issues.

God, I clearly see what I need to do to finally leave home. As I start working through these tasks and revamping my relationship with mom, I'm glad I have a home with friends. It could get rough at times, but the freedom that awaits and the healthier relationship—a friendship—with mom seem worth it. Please be with me. Amen.

FOURTEEN ~

For Women Only

R obin just couldn't say no to her mom, and Toby couldn't understand her difficulty. "Why can't you just get a life with me and without her?" he would say. "She'll be okay." Robin knew on one level that Toby was right, but another part of her would think, *He doesn't understand. How could he? He's a guy.*

➤ ➤ ➤ When have you felt as Robin did? What, like Robin and Toby's Argument #25, tends to prompt those feelings of frustration?

_____

_____

_____

_____

Although men and women are different, they are still more alike than not. Far more crucial than our sexual differences are our character issues. Bear that caveat in mind as you work through this chapter and the next.

LIKE LEAVING LIKE

Page 220   Little girls are more like mom than they are like dad. They share biologies, emotions, and cultural mores with mother in ways that they don't with father. So one of a father's tasks is to help coax his daughters out of the "mom orbit" into the larger world, beginning with himself.

➤ ➤ ➤ What is the earliest memory you have of your relationship with dad? How effective a "father wedge" was he?

_____

_____

_____

_____

➤ ➤ ➤   Which safe people in your life can function like the "father wedge" and help you
keep moving out of the mom orbit without shaming you or being critical of you?

_____

_____

_____

WOMEN AS CONNECTORS

`Page 221`   Women are more connectors at heart than men are. They have more con-
stitutional strengths in bonding, just as men do in aggressiveness. But
being "a lover, not a fighter" brings its own special problems.

➤ ➤ ➤   How is empathy a double-edged sword in your life, especially when it comes to
leaving mom? Be specific about your thoughts and feelings.

_____

_____

_____

_____

➤ ➤ ➤   What will you do to add reality, truthfulness, and responsibility to your character
strengths? Which of your friends will you ask to help you be a loving and honest
person with mom as well as with them?

_____

_____

_____

_____

AGGRESSIVE CONFLICTS

`Page 222`   Women tend to have more problems in the aggressive arena than men;
this can lead to problems with both mom and life in general.

➤ ➤ ➤ With which of the following "aggressive conflicts" do you struggle?

___Assertiveness

___Taking initiative

___Confrontation

___Experiencing and connecting with anger

___Problem solving

___Identity formation

___Setting and keeping boundaries

➤ ➤ ➤ Why can't you say no? Why do you let people run all over you? Or why are you passively compliant? Explore these issues with a counselor or trusted and honest friend.

_____

_____

_____

_____

➤ ➤ ➤ What supportive framework have you developed for your mom work? Who in your life can help you take greater ownership of yourself?

_____

_____

_____

_____

You can grow in healthy aggression. As you do, you'll notice progress in all arenas of life: men, love, and work.

MOTHER ISSUES DISGUISED AS FATHER ISSUES

Page 222 Much work has been done unearthing father issues for people, looking at all the damage dads can do and discovering how to recover from those injuries. But some of this thinking oversimplifies and confuses important issues. Picking bad men isn't always due to having a bad dad, and having a distant father doesn't always create depression.

➤ ➤ ➤   What dad work have you done? Summarize what you've learned about yourself
as you've worked on father issues.

_____

_____

_____

_____

_____

➤ ➤ ➤   Some people believe that all attachment problems are mom problems and that
all aggression problems are dad problems. The logic is that, if a woman has a hard
time setting limits and being her own person, it's because of fathering issues. This
is true, but incompletely so.

❖   Are you dealing more with attachment issues or aggression problems? Be
specific.

_____

_____

_____

_____

❖   What did mom teach you about childhood assertiveness?

_____

_____

_____

_____

❖   What did dad teach you about tenderness?

_____

_____

_____

_____

➤ ➤ ➤ Remember Kristin? Like her, you may think that your "man" problems are "dad" problems.

❖ What "man" problems have you faced or are you currently dealing with?

_____

_____

_____

_____

❖ How are these "man" problems dad problems?

_____

_____

_____

_____

❖ Considering what you've learned about mom's influence, how might mom have contributed to those problems?

_____

_____

_____

_____

Your "man" problems may be "dad" problems, but keep in mind that two dynamics may be in play here: the mother who couldn't let go and the father who couldn't make his little girl feel special. They tend to occur simultaneously.

MOMS AND THEIR LITTLE GIRLS

Page 224 Moms often hold more tightly to their daughters than they do their sons.

➤ ➤ ➤ Have you experienced more of mom's clinginess because of your gender? Give specific examples, especially any contrasts you see between how she deals with you and how she treats a brother.

_____

_____

_____

_____

➤ ➤ ➤ When has or does mom try to make you an ally in conflicts with dad, siblings, or
friends? From this point on, how will you deal with these predicaments?

_____

_____

_____

➤ ➤ ➤ What will you say to mom to help her understand that you want to stay close but
that you also have other friends now and you want her to have her own?

_____

_____

_____

ONLY WOMEN CAN BE MOTHERS

Page 225 This sounds self-evident, but the reality has a great deal of impact on how
you go about working on your mom issues. The strong mothering parts
created in you, a woman, to nurture and protect make a difference in how
you move through your own growth process.

➤ ➤ ➤ *Deal with guilt and anxiety.* If you are a mother, you are in the process of creating and developing life in another person in God's image. It's good for you to see
the weight of your mothering for what it is and treat it as a serious task. But becoming paralyzed by guilt and anxiety will ruin your child. Here are two things
that might help.

❖ 1. Good moms get good mothering.

◆ How do you feel about working on your own character issues? Do you feel
you're being selfish? Responsible? Wise? A good steward? Explain.

_____

_____

_____

_____

◆ From whom are you getting what you didn't receive when you were growing up? Or are you giving from an empty cup?

_____

_____

_____

_____

❖ 2. Good enough vs. perfect.

◆ In what areas of your life are you still trying to be supermom? Why won't you give up that model?

_____

_____

_____

_____

◆ Define "good enough" in your own words. What does a "good enough" mom look like? What does she let go of?

_____

_____

_____

_____

◆ "Good enough" means "adequate but fallible and still growing." It means you want to be

Emotionally present instead of absent/detached
Containing instead of fragile
Supporting separateness instead of resisting it
Accepting badness instead of demanding a Trophy Child
Promoting adulthood instead of keeping your child
Helping your child leave instead of being an American Express Mom

❖ Look at your mothering through the lens of these six traits. In which areas are you headed in the right direction? Where do you need to adjust your trajectory?

_____

_____

_____

_____

➤ ➤ ➤ *Stay in the light of relationship.* It is not enough to prepare for being a fallible, real mom—you need to provide solutions. This might mean making yourself vulnerable and accountable to others who can help you see blind spots in your mothering and support you as you change hurtful ways.

❖ Who in your support group can help you see blind spots in your mothering?

_____

_____

_____

_____

❖ When has some good advice from a trusted friend helped you in your mothering? Recall that experience and let it encourage you to reach out again.

_____

_____

_____

_____

❖ Let that "again" happen soon. What issue(s) with your child(ren) are you currently dealing with? Which point will you talk about with a friend?

_____

_____

_____

_____

➤ ➤ ➤ *Admit your mistakes to your child.* When mom goes to the child, admits failure, asks forgiveness, and changes her own behavior, she truly mothers her child well. When you admit failure, these are some of the healthy dynamics that result:

> You take responsibility for your own badness.
> The burden of your badness is lifted from your child's shoulders and put back where it belongs—onto yours.
> You provide the opportunity for reconciliation.
> You model ownership and forgiveness.
> You take up the slack.

❖ How did your mom deal with mistakes she made? How honest was she with you about her human weaknesses? What did she teach you about making mistakes? About conflict?

_____

_____

_____

_____

❖ How have you been dealing with your mistakes? How honest about your weaknesses are you being?

_____

_____

_____

_____

❖ What will you do the next time you make a mistake? What will you say to your child(ren)?

_____

_____

_____

_____

➤ ➤ ➤ *Give the child some credit.* You might as well admit your weaknesses, because, much of the time, children are aware of our foibles anyway.

❖ What did the story of six-year-old Ricky in the parking lot tell you about kids—their needs as well as their perceptions?

_____

_____

_____

_____

❖ People who are looking at their own issues are always better parents than those who are looking elsewhere. Where have you been looking besides at yourself? What will be your next step in looking at yourself?

_____

_____

_____

_____

As you become the woman God intended you to be, you redeem the mothering you received, and you redemptively pour out your own love into the world. You have a critical and special place in the survival of the family, your religion, the culture, and humanity itself.

God, it really is a struggle for like to leave like, for me to leave mom. And I can't do the work involved—these tasks I've read about—alone. I need friends who will support me, I need to let them support me, I need to continue to pursue the remothering I need. Help me so that I can become the woman you intended me to be. Amen.

FIFTEEN ∼

For Men Only

Have a disagreement, get mad and harsh, walk out instead of "lose." The problem was that Bill had "lost" a lot in the process: customers, relationships, and promotions. But nowhere did the problem bother him as much as in his relationships with women he cared about. He just couldn't seem to make a long-term, romantic relationship work.

➤ ➤ ➤ What of yourself or of the patterns in your life do you see in Bill and the pattern he noticed in his life? Be specific about the similarities.

_____

_____

_____

_____

Many men have patterns similar to Bill's. In his case, a woman's assertiveness led to the conflict. Sometimes it will be a woman's connecting parts that bring about the exit.

➤ ➤ ➤ As soon as love entered the picture, David was gone. The woman's desire for the relationship to become "something more" ended the relationship. Again, what of yourself and your life do you see in David's experience and pattern?

_____

_____

_____

_____

For Bill, when a woman was equal and direct, he was gone. For David, when the relationship got deep, he disappeared. What causes men to leave emotionally if not physically? In this chapter we will look at several reasons why men struggle in their relationships, especially with women, and what that has to do with the mothering process.

LOVE HER, LEAVE HER, RETURN TO HER

Page 236   To understand what is going on with men in their relational world, we must first look at some developmental pattern in their childhood.

➤ ➤ ➤   Review the description of that pattern (pp. 236–38).

    ❖   What details sounded like your growing-up experience?

_____

_____

_____

_____

    ❖   What holes in your growing-up years did this overview help you notice?

_____

_____

_____

_____

➤ ➤ ➤   If men do not do well with mom, they often are not going to do well with the woman they return to—unless the conflicts and stances with mom are worked out first.

    ❖   How well did you do with mom when you were growing up? How well do you do with mom today? Rate your relationship, past and present, on a scale of "10" being the "nice story" of pages 236–38 and "1" being its exact opposite. Explain why your past relationship with mom and your present relationship with her earned the ratings they did.

_____

_____

_____

_____

❖ When men have not gotten what they needed in the mothering process, or they have not used it, or if they have rejected it in some way, they go into their present relationships from either an unfinished or otherwise conflictual stance. What didn't you get, receive, or accept from mom? Be as specific as possible. Then, next to each item on your list, note how you see it influencing your relationships today.

_____

_____

_____

_____

_____

Let's look at how unfinished business with mom specifically affects men.

LOOKING FOR OR AVOIDING NURTURE

Page 238   What do men do when they can't connect? Usually they either avoid intimacy or they fight against it.

➤ ➤ ➤ For David, the fear and the conflict over dependency is still there. When he gets close to a woman and starts to depend on her, then he gets afraid.

❖ If your pattern is like David's, what is the reason behind it?

___ Were you abandoned as a child?
___ Did you have a detached mom?
___ Were you a child who simply could not be comforted?

❖ Theorize the reason behind your fear and conflict over dependency.

❖ When you think back on your childhood and adolescence, what lessons about intimacy were you learning from mom?

_____

_____

_____

_____

➤ ➤ ➤ Aggression and fighting are another way men avoid their dependent longings.

❖ Do you tend to avoid closeness by fighting? Give an example.

_____

_____

_____

_____

❖ Think back on your growing-up years. When did the pattern of using aggression and fighting to avoid intimacy appear?

_____

_____

_____

_____

➤ ➤ ➤ Addictions can be an attempt to finish those dependent longings.

❖ What addictions have you used to replace your need for connection (work, sex, drugs and alcohol, sex, hobbies, sex, food, or something else)?

_____

_____

_____

_____

❖ How helpful have these addictions been? Are they satisfying the need for connection? How have these addictions been harmful?

_____

_____

_____

_____

LOOKING FOR CONTAINMENT

Page 239   If the containing mother failed or was not used, men will look for containment and avoid it at the same time, just as they do with their need to connect.

➤ ➤ ➤   Can you allow your significant other to get close when you are upset? What are you afraid of her seeing, doing, or experiencing if she were to get close?

_____

_____

_____

_____

➤ ➤ ➤   Do you demand containment aggressively? Do you not allow your significant other to leave your side or to have feelings and chaos of her own? How has this behavior impacted your relationships?

_____

_____

_____

_____

DON'T TELL ME WHO TO BE

Page 239   Unless men have good boundaries from their mothering, they will not have a chance with women. They either control, intrude on, and damage women, or they feel controlled and smothered by them.

➤ ➤ ➤   What is your tendency with women—to control, intrude on, and damage them or to feel controlled and smothered by them? What does your answer suggest about how strong your boundaries are with mom?

_____

_____

_____

_____

➤ ➤ ➤ Kevin had never established boundaries with his own mom. So even though he
adored his wife, he was not strong enough in his own boundaries to say no to her.
Where do you see yourself in Kevin's experience?

_____

_____

_____

_____

➤ ➤ ➤ What are you doing to turn, "Stop controlling me!" into "No, I don't want to"?

_____

_____

_____

_____

THE PERFECT WOMAN

`Page 240`   Tom had not fully integrated his own imperfections into a realistic picture
of who he is. He could not accept all of himself, both good and bad, so he
could not accept imperfections in others.

➤ ➤ ➤ Are you on a quest for the perfect woman? What is your realistic estimation of
how feasible or futile your quest is? If you deem it futile, why do you continue to
pursue the perfect woman?

_____

_____

_____

_____

➤ ➤ ➤ Unresolved integration is also evidenced by men who require their women to
mirror their wishes to be ideal. They demand worship and idealization instead of
real love that includes their imperfections. How do you respond to criticism, especially from a woman?

_____

_____

_____

_____

➤ ➤ ➤ What did you learn about mistakes, failures, and imperfections from mom?

_____

_____

_____

➤ ➤ ➤ What are you doing to learn to accept your imperfections?

_____

_____

_____

AMERICAN EXPRESS PAYMENTS

`Page 241`   If you have never "left home," you will not find a truly satisfying relationship with a woman or fulfill your career aspirations. You still have too many control and security issues.

➤ ➤ ➤ In general, how do you respond when women assert themselves? Do you resent them, or do you give in to their control and remain a little boy? Give a specific example or two from your life.

_____

_____

_____

➤ ➤ ➤ Do you look to women to provide basic security instead of feeling secure in yourself? Again give a specific example from life and comment on how effective a woman is as a source of security.

_____

_____

_____

_____

➤ ➤ ➤   What are you doing to leave home?

_____

_____

_____

_____

STILL-THE-BOSS MOM ISSUES

Page 242   As we saw at the beginning of this chapter, Bill had never become an equal with women.

➤ ➤ ➤   Feeling "one down" to your own mother can prompt you to fight whenever you encounter an assertive woman. Is this your pattern? If so, give an example or two.

_____

_____

_____

_____

➤ ➤ ➤   What trouble has your "dominate or be dominated" approach to life caused?

_____

_____

_____

_____

➤ ➤ ➤   What are you doing to learn to feel equal instead of one down or one up to women?

_____

_____

_____

_____

SAY IT AGAIN

Page 242
All of these issues really say the same thing over again: If you, a man, are not finished with mothering, you are going to have problems, and those problems are going to get you into conflicts, particularly in your relationships with women. The problem is ultimately one of regression.

➤ ➤ ➤ Think about a recent conflict in a relationship with a woman. How did you regress in that situation? Be as specific as possible.

_____

_____

_____

_____

➤ ➤ ➤ As you deal with your unfinished mothering, what can a support group offer you that a dating relationship or marriage can't? Where will you, if you haven't already, find a support group?

_____

_____

_____

_____

SPECIFIC STYLES OF AVOIDING RESOLVING MOTHER ISSUES

Page 243
Men are very good at leaving mother issues unresolved. But the whole idea of resolving mother issues is to find good mothering, bring all of your different parts to the relationship appropriately, and thus integrate as a person.

➤ ➤ ➤ Which of the following do you still need to integrate?

____ Needy feelings
____ Dependent feelings
____ Assertive boundary setting
____ Respect for others' boundaries

___ Imperfections
___ Forgiving others' imperfections
___ Sexual feelings
___ Talents
___ Thoughts and opinions

➤ ➤ ➤ What is keeping you from doing the remothering work? Or, if you've already begun, what is keeping you going?

_____

_____

_____

_____

➤ ➤ ➤ The alternative to being all of yourself with a woman is to be different parts of yourself with different women. This is called splitting. Which of the following do you struggle with? (See the descriptions on pages 244–45.)

___ Love-Sex Split
___ Fusion-Unavailable Split
___ Use One/Respect Another
___ Moral-Immoral

➤ ➤ ➤ *Extremes.* In trying to prevent regression, men usually revert to one of two immature styles: aggression or pleasing. When have you either become hostile to ward off conflicts or, acting like a little boy, complied and fused with women?

_____

_____

_____

_____

➤ ➤ ➤ *The Answer.* The answer to splitting is to learn to be all of yourself with women. Bring your needs, your strengths, your skills, your weaknesses, your bad parts, your grief, your sexuality, and all of the rest of you into relationship. This is how integration takes place.

❖ Which of the parts of you listed are you most reluctant to share with a woman?

_____

_____

_____

_____

❖ Begin working toward integration right now. To what safe relationship will you bring all of yourself? After all, to be known is to be made whole.

_____

_____

_____

_____

WHAT ABOUT DAD?

Page 246   Some men who have not finished with mom have a father problem.

➤ ➤ ➤ A boy's attachment to his male role models gives him strength to stand up to women.

❖ What male role models did you have as a child? What lessons, values, attitudes, and behaviors did you learn from them?

_____

_____

_____

_____

❖ What male role models did you have during your teenage years? What lessons, values, attitudes, and behaviors did you learn from them?

_____

_____

_____

_____

❖ What do your answers suggest about one reason you have unfinished mom work?

_____

_____

_____

_____

➤ ➤ ➤ What men in your support systems can you use as role models to help you in your healing process with mom?

_____

_____

_____

_____

➤ ➤ ➤ *Being a Nurturing Father.* The more you make yourself emotionally available to your wife and children, the fewer mother problems they will have. What will you do to love your wife? To be a good dad?

_____

_____

_____

_____

GROW UP

Page 247

Men, there is only one way to summarize all of this—grow up. If you still have unfinished business with mother, you would do well to begin working on those issues so you can treat your woman well and succeed in your career.

➤ ➤ ➤ What good counselor can you work with? Or where can you go for a recommendation?

_____

_____

_____

➤ ➤ ➤ What support system is available to you? What will you do to strengthen it?

_____

_____

_____

_____

➤ ➤ ➤ What good male role models are around? Where will you go to find some?

_____

_____

_____

_____

➤ ➤ ➤ Where will you find some good women to stand by you in this process?

_____

_____

_____

_____

If you can get the mothering you need, work out the issues with your real mom, leave the dependent stance, and return to women as equals, you will find true fulfillment at the end of your journey. As God said, "It is not good for man to be alone."

God, a lot of this is against-the-cultural-grain stuff—this talk about dependency and intimacy. And then there are the boundaries, confrontation, and equality with women issues. It's really clear that I missed some key things growing up. I'm not finished with mothering. Please help me finish that work. Amen.

SIXTEEN ⟞

What About Now?

W e hope we haven't "mom bashed" but rather, have helped you become more aware of yourself and take responsibility for yourself in new ways.

➤ ➤ ➤ Summarize what you've become aware of about the following from working through *The Mom Factor*.

❖ Your own childhood

_____
_____
_____
_____

❖ Your present character growth issues and tasks

_____
_____
_____
_____

❖ Your present relationship with mother

_____
_____
_____
_____

❖ Your present relationships with others

_____
_____
_____
_____

❖ Your own parenting issues

_____
_____
_____
_____

➤ ➤ ➤ If we were to describe our intent in this book with one word, it would be *recon-ciliation*. When people are reconciled, they are restored to those from whom they were alienated and they are able to reconnect.

❖ What kind of reconciliation are you facing? (See descriptions on pages 250–51.)

Reconciliation between yourself and mother

_____
_____

Reconciliation within yourself

_____
_____

Reconciliation with your safe relationships

_____
_____

Reconciliation to responsibility

_____
_____

Reconciliation to God

_____

_____

➤ ➤ ➤ What action steps do you need to take in each area of reconciliation necessary in your life?

❖ Reconciliation between you and your mother

—Invite mom into the reconciliation process.
—Forgive her for her mistakes.
—Ask her forgiveness for your responses to her.
—Bring hurtful issues from childhood into the present.
—Get unmet needs met by other people.
—Move into a mutual friendship with mom.
—Set limits with mom.
—Develop the relationship the way friends do.

❖ Reconciliation within yourself

__Heal a hurt from your childhood.
__Accept realities of the past and grieve them now.
__Give up your own desires and wishes for that which can never be—things such as a close relationship with mom, her encouragement of your God-given separate identity, her acceptance of the "real you," her viewing you as a grown-up, or her owning and taking responsibility for her character limitations.
__Get unmet needs met by others.

❖ Reconciliation with your safe relationships

—Stay connected to your remothering people.
—Keep short accounts with your remothering people.
—Value them.
—Let them love you.
—Love them.
—Be open to them.
—Heed them.

❖ Reconciliation to responsibility

—Stop denying your issues.
—Stop blaming mom, God, circumstances, or others.
—Begin the long journey of repair.
—Choose love, not isolation; life, not death; light, not darkness; truth, not deception.

❖ Reconciliation to God

—Connect or reconnect with God, the Reconciler.
—Ask God for forgiveness.
—Read the Bible.
—Pray and listen to God.

Our reconciliation to God forms the very foundation for our ability to forgive and to reconnect, not only with God but with mom, others, and ourselves. Reconciliation transforms us into the loving and working people we were intended to be.

God, all along I've been aware of the hugeness of the task. I'm glad that you, the Reconciler, can help me along this path. May I learn from you to be aware of self—aware of the loving and working person you intend me to be; to take responsibility for my actions, attitudes, words, failures, past, and present; and to work on reconciliation wherever it needs to happen. I look forward to growing and becoming the person you made me to be. Amen.

For information about tapes, speaking engagements, a resource catalogue, or
a Cloud-Townsend seminar near you, call 1-800-676-HOPE, or write:

Cloud-Townsend Communications
260 Newport Center Drive, #430
Newport Beach, CA 92660

Discover the path to true inner healing and spiritual growth through these additional titles from Drs. Henry Cloud and John Townsend.

Boundaries: When to Say Yes, When to Say No, to Take Control of Your Life
Hardcover: 0-310-58590-2   Workbook: 0-310-49481-8
Audio: 0-310-58598-8   Curriculum 0-310-58599-6

Safe People: How to Find Relationships That Are Good for You and Avoid Those That Aren't
Softcover: 0-310-21084-4   Audio: 0-310-59568-1
Workbook: 0-310-49501-6

Twelve "Christian" Beliefs That Can Drive You Crazy: Relief from False Assumptions
Softcover: 0-310-49491-5   Audio: 0-310-59578-9

The Mom Factor: Dealing with the Mother You Had, Didn't Have, or Still Contend With
Hardcover: 0-310-20036-9   Audio: 0-310-20453-4

Also by Dr. Henry Cloud
Changes That Heal: How to Understand Your Past to Ensure a Healthier Future
Softcover: 0-310-60631-4   Audio: 0-310-20567-0
Mass Market: 0-06-104345-1   Workbook: 0-310-60633-0

Also by Dr. John Townsend
Hiding from Love: How to Change the Withdrawal Patterns That Isolate and Imprison You
Softcover: 0-310-20107-1

ZondervanPublishingHouse
Grand Rapids, Michigan

A Division of HarperCollinsPublishers

We want to hear from you. Please send your comments about this book
to us in care of the address below. Thank you.

ZondervanPublishingHouse
Grand Rapids, Michigan 49530
http://www.zondervan.com